Task
MATHS
1

BARBARA BALL & DEREK BALL

Nelson

Thomas Nelson and Sons Ltd
Nelson House Mayfield Road
Walton-on-Thames Surrey
KT12 5PL UK

51 York Place
Edinburgh
EH1 3JD UK

Thomas Nelson (Hong Kong) Ltd
Toppan Building 10/F
22A Westlands Road
Quarry Bay Hong Kong

Thomas Nelson Australia
102 Dodds Street
South Melbourne
Victoria 3205 Australia

Nelson Canada
1120 Birchmount Road
Scarborough Ontario
MIK 5G4 Canada

Published by Thomas Nelson and Sons Ltd. 1993

ISBN 0-17-431162-1
NPN 9 8 7 6 5 4 3 2

Printed in Hong Kong.

Acknowedgements

The authors are grateful to all those teachers and students who have helped by trialling the material in this book. They value, in particular, the frequent and most helpful advice they received from Clyde Banks, Louise Furre, Ros Holden, Ann Meredith, Ian Robinson, Adrian Smith, Phillip Whiffing, Trevor Weight and Clare Whittaker.

They would also like to thank Ian Robinson and his year 7 class at Beaumont Leys School, Leicester for their help with some of the photographs.

The authors and publisher are grateful to Juliet and Charles Snape for their kind permission to reproduce 'A Christmas Puzzle' on page 67. Thanks are due to the following for the permission to reproduce photographs by: David Bamber on pages 6, 12, 13, 15, 16, 20, 21, 24, 26, 44, 57, 62, 79, 82, 101, 102 ,114, 115, 135, 138, 143, 156, 159; and Valerie Randall on pages 13, 17, 24, 25, 35, 39, 40, 54, 55, 58, 59, 78, 100, 103, 105, 107, 113, 119, 121, 138, 139, 140, 149, 154, 155, 161, 162, and 167.

While every effort has been made to trace and acknowledge copyright holders, in some cases this has not been possible. Should any infringement have occurred, the publishers tender their apologies and welcome any information which would remedy the situation.

CONTENTS

1 MONTY

Look at the number grid below. It has three pythons lying on it.

1	2	3	4	5	6	7	8	9	10
11	12	13	14	15	16	17	18	19	20
21	22	23	24	25	26	27	28	29	30
31	32	33	34	35	36	37	38	39	40
41	42	43	44	45	46	47	48	49	50
51	52	53	54	55	56	57	58	59	60
61	62	63	64	65	66	67	68	69	70
71	72	73	74	75	76	77	78	79	80
81	82	83	84	85	86	87	88	89	90
91	92	93	94	95	96	97	98	99	100

All the pythons are called Monty.

All Montys are seven squares long.

Monty can be curled up or stretched out.

LOTS OF MONTYS

Draw some Montys.

Make all your Montys different shapes.

See how many different shapes your class can get if everyone shares their ideas.

You can make Montys from interlocking cubes.

YOU COULD USE:

Monty, the python, is the star of a computer program called *Monty*.

You could use this computer program. Monty lies on the grid and you have to say what numbers are in his body.

WHAT IS THE DIFFERENCE?

You will need a number grid for this activity.

Look at the red Monty in the picture below.

Look at the number in his head and the number in his tail.

Now look at the blue Monty.

Difference is
42 − 22 = 20.

1	2	3	4	5	6	7	8	9	10
11	12	13	14	15	16	17	18	19	20
21	22	23	24	25	26	27	28	29	30
31	32	33	34	35	36	37	38	39	40
41	42	43	44	45	46	47	48	49	50
51	52	53	54	55	56	57	58	59	60
61	62	63	64	65	66	67	68	69	70
71	72	73	74	75	76	77	78	79	80
81	82	83	84	85	86	87	88	89	90
91	92	93	94	95	96	97	98	99	100

Difference is
90 − 57 = 33.

1 Draw some Montys on your number grid. Write down the difference for each Monty.

2 Can you draw a Monty where the difference is 4?
Can you draw a Monty where the difference is 27?

3 What is the smallest possible difference? What is the largest?

4 What is the smallest possible *odd number* difference?
What is the largest?

5 The picture below shows two Montys which are the same shape.
The difference for the green Monty is 42.
The difference for the orange Monty is 16.

1	2	3	4	5	6	7	8	9	10
11	12	13	14	15	16	17	18	19	20
21	22	23	24	25	26	27	28	29	30
31	32	33	34	35	36	37	38	39	40
41	42	43	44	45	46	47	48	49	50
51	52	53	54	55	56	57	58	59	60
61	62	63	64	65	66	67	68	69	70
71	72	73	74	75	76	77	78	79	80
81	82	83	84	85	86	87	88	89	90
91	92	93	94	95	96	97	98	99	100

Draw several Montys on a number grid. All the Montys you draw must be the same shape. They do not all have to be the same way up.

How many different differences can you find for your Montys?

6 If you know the difference for one Monty, can you predict the differences for other Montys which are the same shape?

TOTAL MONTY

You will need a number grid sheet for this activity.

Add up the numbers in each of the Montys in the picture below.

1	2	3	4	5	6	7	8	9	10
11	12	13	14	15	16	17	18	19	20
21	22	23	24	25	26	27	28	29	30
31	32	33	34	35	36	37	38	39	40
41	42	43	44	45	46	47	48	49	50
51	52	53	54	55	56	57	58	59	60
61	62	63	64	65	66	67	68	69	70
71	72	73	74	75	76	77	78	79	80
81	82	83	84	85	86	87	88	89	90
91	92	93	94	95	96	97	98	99	100

Total is 149.

Total is 573.

1 Draw a Monty on your number grid. Find the total of the numbers in Monty's body.

For question 2 you might find it useful to draw your Monty on tracing paper or acetate.

2 What happens to the total when Monty stays the same shape but moves to the *right*?
What if he moves *down*?
Or *up*?
Or to the *left*?

What happens if he moves four squares to the left? Or five squares down?

1	2	3	4	5	6	7	8	9	10
11	12	13	14	15	16	17	18	19	20
21	22	23	24	25	26	27	28	29	30
31	32	33	34	35	36	37	38	39	40
41	42	43	44	45	46	47	48	49	50
51	52	53	54	55	56	57	58	59	60
61	62	63	64	65	66	67	68	69	70
71	72	73	74	75	76	77	78	79	80
81	82	83	84	85	86	87	88	89	90
91	92	93	94	95	96	97	98	99	100

Monty moves five squares down.

3 A Monty is hiding somewhere on the grid. The total of the numbers in Monty's body is 37.

What are the numbers in Monty's body?

4 A Monty is hiding somewhere on the grid. One of the numbers in his body is 28.

What is the total of the numbers in Monty's body?

You cannot *know* the answer to this question. But find two *possible* answers.

Now find the smallest possible answer.

Find the largest possible answer.

MEAN MONTY

You will need a number grid sheet for this activity.

 Look at the red Monty.

The total of the numbers in Monty's body is 168.

Divide this number by 7. You get 24.

24 is the **mean** (or **average**) of the numbers in this Monty's body.

1	2	3	4	5	6	7	8	9	10
11	12	13	14	15	16	17	18	19	20
21	22	23	24	25	26	27	28	29	30
31	32	33	34	35	36	37	38	39	40
41	42	43	44	45	46	47	48	49	50
51	52	53	54	55	56	57	58	59	60
61	62	63	64	65	66	67	68	69	70
71	72	73	74	75	76	77	78	79	80
81	82	83	84	85	86	87	88	89	90
91	92	93	94	95	96	97	98	99	100

Look at the blue Monty.

The total of the numbers in Monty's body is 408.

Divide this number by 7. You get 58.3 approximately.

58.3 is the **mean** of the numbers in this Monty's body.

1 Draw some Montys and find their mean numbers.

2 Draw a Monty which has 58 as its mean number.

3 Draw a Monty which has 26 as its mean number.

4 Draw a Monty whose mean number is a *whole number*.

Draw another Monty of a *different shape* whose mean number is a whole number.

And another. And another.

Is there anything special about the shapes of these Montys?

MONTY MULTIPLES

You will need a number grid sheet for this activity.

 In this grid the **multiples** of 3 have been coloured red.

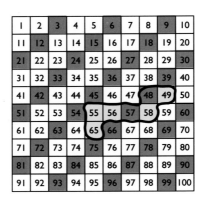

1 Shade or colour the multiples of 3 on a number grid.

2 The Monty on the red grid has *two* red squares inside him.

   Another Monty is hiding on the red grid. What is the smallest number of red squares he could have inside him?

3 The largest number of red squares a Monty could have inside him is *four*.

   Draw a Monty with four red squares inside him.

   How many different shapes could Monty be to have four red squares inside him?

 In this grid the **multiples** of 4 have been coloured blue.

4 The Monty on the blue grid has three blue squares inside him.

   Another Monty is hiding on the blue grid. What is the smallest number of blue squares he could have inside him?

5 Another Monty is hiding on the blue grid. What is the largest number of blue squares he could have inside him?

   How many different shapes could Monty be for this biggest number of blue squares?

6 Colour in your own grids. Colour in multiples of 2. Or 5. Or 6. Or 7. Or 8. Or …

   For each grid, find the smallest and largest number of squares that could be inside Monty's body.

A SQUARE MEAL

1	2	3	4	5	6	7	8	9	10
11	12	13	14	15	16	17	18	19	20
21	22	23	24	25	26	27	28	29	30
31	32	33	34	35	36	37	38	39	40
41	42	43	44	45	46	47	48	49	50
51	52	53	54	55	56	57	58	59	60
61	62	63	64	65	66	67	68	69	70
71	72	73	74	75	76	77	78	79	80
81	82	83	84	85	86	87	88	89	90
91	92	93	94	95	96	97	98	99	100

You will need a number grid sheet for this activity.

I The Monty on this grid has three **square** numbers in his body.

One of the square numbers in Monty is 36.
36 is a square number because $36 = 6 \times 6$.

1 Look at the Monty on the grid. What are the three square numbers in Monty's body?

2 Draw a Monty which has one square number inside him.

3 Draw a Monty which has just two square numbers inside him.

4 A Monty is hiding on the grid. The square numbers in his body add up to 50.

What are the square numbers in his body?

A1 page 22

WHERE IS MONTY?

1 A Monty is hiding on a number grid. Here are some clues to find where he is.

- Monty has exactly one bend in him.
- All the numbers in Monty have a 5 in them.
- The smallest number in Monty is 53.

Where is Monty?

2 Monty has now moved and is hiding somewhere else on the grid. Here are some clues to tell you where he is.

- All the numbers in Monty have a 2 in them.
- The biggest number is 42.

3 Monty has moved again. Here are some clues to tell you where he is.

- He is in the bottom half of the grid.
- There are two square numbers inside his body.
- One of the numbers in his body is a multiple of 5.
- One of the numbers in his body is a multiple of 14.

4 Monty has moved again. The total of the numbers in Monty's body is 109. This time there are several possible answers. How many answers can you find?

5 Now choose where to draw a Monty. Make up your own clues for someone else to discover where your Monty is hiding.
You can make up clues to explain *exactly* where he is.
Or you can make up clues with more than one answer.

2 HOW BIG IS YOUR CLASSROOM?

HOW BIG IS YOUR CLASSROOM?

You could answer this question in different ways.

One way is to find out how much will fit into your classroom.

1 How many people are there in your classroom now?

2 How many chairs are there in your classroom?
How many tables?

3 How many legs are there in your classroom?

HOW BIG IS THE CLASSROOM FLOOR?

The classroom floor could be measured in many different ways.
Here are some ideas.

1 How many sheets of newspaper would you need to cover the classroom floor completely?

2 How many tables could fit in your classroom?
(Each table must have all its legs in contact with the floor.)

3 How many people could stand on the floor of your classroom at the same time?

4 How many people could lie on the floor of your classroom at the same time?

5 Make a square with sides of length exactly one metre. Make it by sticking together sheets of newspaper.

How many of these squares would you need to cover the floor of your classroom?

(You are allowed to cut the squares up to make them fit better.)

FILLING THE ROOM

1 How many tables could be fitted into your classroom, if they were piled up to the ceiling?

2 How many chairs could be fitted in?

3 Make a cube with sides of length one metre. How many of these cubes would fit into your classroom?

HOW MANY?

1 (*a*) How many Mars bars could you fit onto your table top (without piling them up)?

(*b*) How many Mars bars could fit onto the floor of your classroom?

(*c*) How many Mars bars could you fit into your classroom?

2 How many tennis balls could you fit into your classroom?

3 Choose an object.

How many of your objects could you fit into your classroom?

A PICTURE OF YOUR CLASSROOM

Draw a picture of your classroom.

● Your picture could show the shape and size of your classroom.

● You could draw a picture of the classroom floor.

You could use squared paper.

You could think of a way to explain how big the classroom floor actually is.

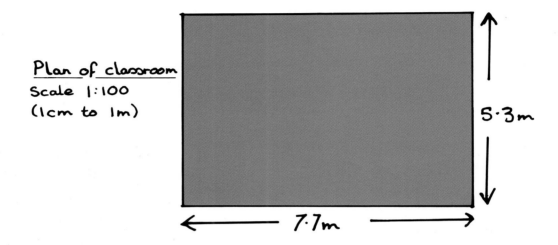

Plan of classroom
Scale 1:100
(1cm to 1m)

5·3m

7·7m

● You could draw a picture of the walls of your classroom. Or the ceiling.

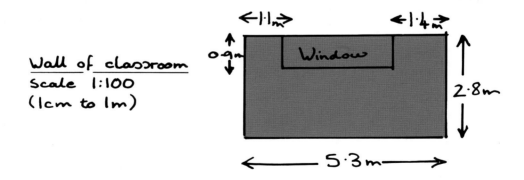

Wall of classroom
Scale 1:100
(1cm to 1m)

←1·1m→   ←1·4m→
0·9m   Window   2·8m
5·3m

● You could make a model of your classroom.

A2 page 22   G20 page 116

LAYING OUT YOUR CLASSROOM

The furniture in a classroom can be arranged in different ways.

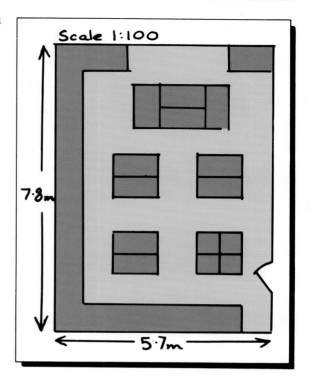

Scale 1:100

7.8m

5.7m

The photograph shows a classroom where people work in groups of four. The plan shows how the tables are arranged.

1   Draw a plan of your classroom.

Show the tables and chairs on your plan.

- You will have to measure the size of the tables and chairs.
- You will also have to measure the size of the gaps between them.

2   Could you rearrange your classroom, so that people work in groups of four?

Here is how you can find out.

- Draw shapes for the chairs and table in your classroom. Think about what size these shapes should be.
- Cut the shapes out and arrange them on your plan of your classroom.
- Remember to leave room for people to sit on chairs and to stick out their elbows.

3   Could you rearrange your classroom, so that people work in groups of six?

4   Could you rearrange your classroom, so that everyone sits individually facing the front?

5   Could you rearrange your classroom, so that everyone sits in one big group?

3 BIRTHDAYS

WHEN WERE YOU BORN?

1 Collect the birthdays of all the people in your class. Include the year of the birthday as well as the day and the month.

2 Which day of the week were you born? You might already know this. Or you might need to work it out. There are various ways of doing this.

Here is one way. Some of the people in your class probably know for certain which day of the week they were born. You can work out your day from one of theirs. Choose someone with a birthday near to yours.

Collect the birth days of the week for the whole class.

YOU COULD USE:

You could use a database to help you store and display the information you have collected.

Some database programs, such as *Pinpoint*, help you to produce a questionnaire for people to fill in.

BIRTHDAYS

What is your name? _____

When were you born ___/___/___

In what season were you born? ☐ Spring ☐ Autumn
☐ Summer ☐ Winter

On what day of the week were you born? ☐ Monday ☐ Friday
☐ Tuesday ☐ Saturday
☐ Wednesday ☐ Sunday
☐ Thursday

A database program such as *Pinpoint* can be used to produce bar charts, pie charts, percentages, and results such as median, mean and range.

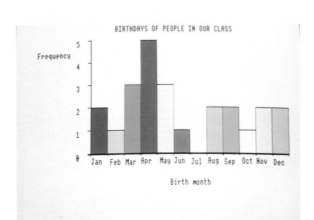

BIRTHDAYS OF PEOPLE IN OUR CLASS

THE MOST POPULAR TIME TO BE BORN

1 Which is the most popular month for birthdays in your class?

Produce a tally chart showing the number of people born in each month. Use your tally chart to draw a bar chart.

Month	Tally	Total
JAN	//	2
FEB	///	3
MAR	///	3
APR	//	2
MAY	///	3
JUN	//	2
JULY	///	3
AUG	/	1
SEP	/	1
OCT	///	3
NOV	///	3
DEC	//	2

Number of people in the class born each month

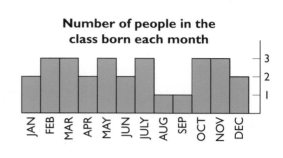

2 How many people in your class were born in spring? How many in summer? How many in autumn? How many in winter?

Would you expect the same number of people to be born in spring, summer, autumn and winter? Is this true for your class?

Before you can answer question 2, you have to know when spring is. When does spring start and end? Different people say different things. You need to be clear about what *you* are saying.

3 If you are interested in astrology you could work out the number of people in your class for each birth sign.

Capricorn	22 December–20 January	Cancer	22 June–23 July
Aquarius	21 January–19 February	Leo	24 July–23 August
Pisces	20 February–20 March	Virgo	24 August–23 September
Aries	21 March–20 April	Libra	24 September–23 October
Taurus	21 April–21 May	Scorpio	24 October–22 November
Gemini	22 May–21 June	Sagittarius	23 November–21 December

MONDAY'S CHILD

Monday's child is full of grace
Tuesday's child is fair of face
Wednesday's child is full of woe
Thursday's child has far to go
Friday's child is loving and giving
Saturday's child works hard for a living
But the child that is born on the Sabbath day
Is loving and pure and good and gay.

1 How many people in your class were born on a Monday? A Tuesday? A Wednesday? … Draw a bar chart to display the results.

2 How many people in your class would you *expect* to have been born on a Monday?

How many people in the whole school would you expect to have been born on a Monday?

How many people in Britain would you expect to have been born on a Monday?

 The population of Britain is about 57 million.

HOW OLD ARE YOU?

People usually give their age as a whole number of years. They say

You *might* get a different answer to question 1, depending on whether you count only the number of completed months or give your answer to the nearest month.

1 Sometimes people ask for your age in years and months. How many years and months old are you?

18

These are leap years:

1976, 1980, 1984, 1988, 1992, 1996, 2000, 2004, 2008, …

There are 365 days in a year.
There are 366 days in a leap year.

The number of days in a month:

January	31	May	31	September	30
February	28 or 29	June	30	October	31
March	31	July	31	November	30
April	30	August	31	December	31

There are 24 hours in a day.
There are 60 minutes in an hour.
There are 60 seconds in a minute.

You can only give your age accurately to the nearest day, if you know what time of day you were born.

2 How many days old are you? Don't forget leap years!

Give your answer to someone else. Get them to work out when your birthday is.

 3 Collect the answers to questions 1 and 2 for the whole class.

If you are using a computer database you could put these answers into it.

4 How many hours old are you? How many minutes? How many seconds? How *accurate* are your answers?

Remember: if you carry on with this work tomorrow the answers will be different!

B7
page
39

YOUR CLASS AS A WHOLE

1 Which person in your class are you closest to in age? What is the difference in your ages?

 The **range** means the difference in age between the oldest and youngest.

---

2 Who is the oldest in your class? Who is the youngest? What is the *range* of ages in your class?

3 Write out a list of all the people in your class in order of age.

The **median** age of your class is the age of the middle person in your class.

You could get everyone in your class to stand in a line in order of age.

Suppose there is an *even* number of people in your class. There will be two people in the *middle*. They will probably be different ages. What do you think the **median** age should be?

---

4 Who is the person with the middle age in your class? What is the *median* age of your class?

 To find the **mean** age you *add up* all the ages and *divide* by the number of people in your class.

---

5 What is the *mean* age of your class?

6 Either the *median* age or the *mean* age can be used as an average age for your class.

Are you older or younger than average for your class?

7 How old is your teacher? If you include your teacher in your class how will the *median* age change? How will the *mean* age change?

Teachers might not want to tell you how old they are. If your teacher does tell you, you can work out the *median* and *mean* age including your teacher. If not, you can still work out one of them. Which one?

PERCENTAGES

Working out percentages

Suppose you have 28 people in your class.
Suppose 6 of them were born in spring.

To find the percentage who were born in spring you need a calculator. You divide 6 by 28 and then multiply by 100

| 6 | ÷ | 2 | 8 | × | 1 | 0 | 0 | = |

This gives 21.428571.

So 21% of the class were born in the spring.

1 Find the percentage of people in your class who were born in spring.
And in summer.
And in autumn.
And in winter.

Find the percentage of people in your class who were born on a Wednesday.
And on other days.

2 What percentage of the whole population of Britain would you expect to have been born in spring?

Or to have been born on a Wednesday?

3 Draw a pie chart to show the number of people in your class who were born in each season.

And who were born on each day of the week.

If you are using a database such as *Pinpoint*, the computer will draw your pie charts for you.

If not, use the resource sheet called *'Percentage pie charts'*.

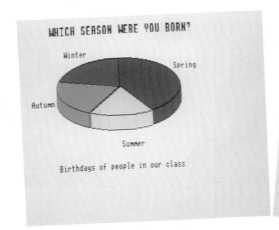

WHICH SEASON WERE YOU BORN?

Winter   Spring

Autumn

Summer

Birthdays of people in our class

WHICH DAY OF THE WEEK WERE YOU BORN?

Sunday   Monday

Saturday

Friday   Tuesday

Thursday   Wednesday

Birthdays of people in our class

A3
page
23

D11
page
68

REVIEW EXERCISES A

EXERCISE 1 Number 1

> Do not use a calculator until you have to.

1 Work out the following:

(a) 16 + 14	(e) 100 − 50	(i) 2 × 6
(b) 26 + 14	(f) 100 − 49	(j) 2 × 7
(c) 26 + 15	(g) 100 − 51	(k) 4 × 7
(d) 36 + 15	(h) 100 − 61	(l) 40 × 7

2 Arrange these numbers in order. Put the smallest number first.

71, 21, 19, 23, 38, 100, 10

3

Gadstown School	
	Number of students
Year 7	141
Year 8	153
Year 9	134
Year 10	125
Year 11	110
Total	?

What is the total number of students in the school?

4

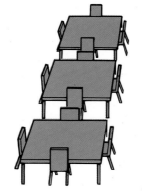 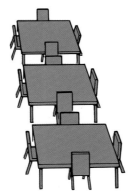

(a) How many legs altogether?
(b) Now each chair has someone sitting on it. How many legs are there altogether?

5 (a) Write down five multiples of 3.
(b) How many multiples of 3 are less than 50?
(c) How many multiples of 3 are less than 100?
(d) How many multiples of 3 are less than 1000?

6 I am thinking of a number.
The number is less than 100.
The *square* of the number ends in 6.
What number am I thinking of?
(There is more than one possible answer.)

7 I am thinking of a number.
The number is between 40 and 50.
The number is a multiple of 7.
The number is not a square number.
What number am I thinking of?

8 What is the biggest square number with two digits?
What is the biggest square number with three digits?

EXERCISE 2 Plans

> You might want to use centimetre-squared paper for questions 2, 3 and 4.

1 Here is an accurate plan of a classroom floor. In the plan 1 centimetre represents 1 metre.

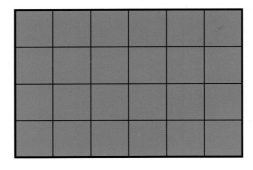

(a) What is the length of the classroom?
(b) What is the width of the classroom?
(c) What is the perimeter of the classroom?
(d) What is the area of the classroom floor?

2 Here is a rough sketch of a classroom.

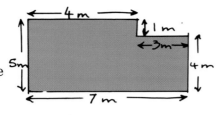

Using a scale of 1 cm to represent 1 metre, draw an accurate plan of the classroom.

3 Here is a rough sketch of a school hall.

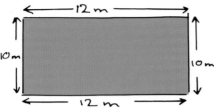

Using a scale of 1 cm to represent 4 metres, draw an accurate plan of the hall.

4 Measure the table or desk you are writing on. Choose a suitable scale and draw a plan of the table.

5 A playing field is a rectangle, measuring 130 metres by 200 metres. What scale would you use to fit a plan of the field onto the paper you are writing on? (You need not draw the plan.)

EXERCISE 3 Handling data 1

30 daisies were collected. The number of petals on each daisy was counted. Here are the results.
35, 44, 31, 50, 46, 35, 54, 39, 42, 33, 54, 33, 51, 50, 47, 47, 54, 36, 34, 54, 50, 40, 40, 31, 40, 39, 39, 50, 50, 31

1 (*a*) Copy and complete this tally chart.

Number of petals	Tally	Total
30–33		
34–37		
38–41		
42–45		
46–49		
50–53		
54–57		

(*b*) Draw a bar graph to display the information on your tally chart. Label the bar graph carefully.

2 Find the median number of petals for the 30 daisies.

3 Find the mean number of petals for the 30 daisies.

4 Find the range of the numbers of petals for the 30 daisies.

> For question 5 you need the resource sheet 'Percentage pie charts'.

5 (*a*) How many daisies had an odd number of petals?
(*b*) How many daisies had an even number of petals?
(*c*) What percentage of daisies had an odd number of petals?
(*d*) Draw a pie chart to show this result.

6 Suppose that only 10 daisies had been collected. You would only have the first 10 numbers of petals.

(*a*) What would the median have been then?
(*b*) What would the mean have been then?
(*c*) What would the range have been then?

7 The 30 daisies were collected from a field where there were thousands of daisies.

(*a*) Would the range for the number of petals on all the daisies be bigger or smaller than the range for the 30 daisies?
(*b*) Would the median for the number of petals on all the daisies be bigger or smaller than the median for the 30 daisies?
(*c*) Would the mean for the number of petals on all the daisies be bigger or smaller than the mean for the 30 daisies?
(*d*) If you want to estimate the mean number of petals on all the daisies in the field, is it better to collect 10 daisies or 30 daisies?

Explain your answer.

4 HALVING

WHAT IS A HALF?

Look at the pictures on this page.
Explain how each picture shows a half.

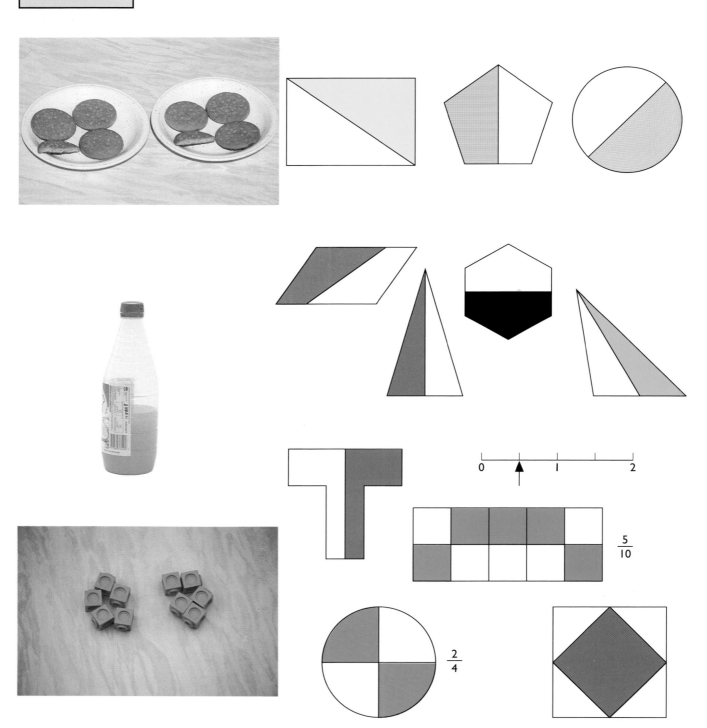

DRAW HALF

You could work with someone else for this activity.

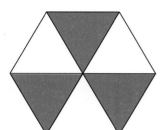

$\frac{3}{6}$

1 Draw a shape. Get someone else to colour $\frac{1}{2}$ of it. Get them to explain why it is half.

2 Draw a shape. Get someone else to colour $\frac{2}{4}$ of it. Get them to explain why it is $\frac{2}{4}$. Now explain to them why it is a half.

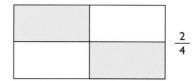

$\frac{2}{4}$

3 Draw a shape. Get someone else to colour $\frac{3}{6}$ of it. Get them to explain why it is $\frac{3}{6}$. Now explain to them why it is half.

4 Now do the same for $\frac{4}{8}$.
And $\frac{5}{10}$.

FIND HALF

I		
1 metre = 100 centimetres	1 m = 100 cm	
1 metre = 1000 millimetres	1 m = 1000 mm	
1 kilogram = 1000 g	1 kg = 1000 g	
1 litre = 1000 cubic centimetres	1 l = 1000 cm³	
1 pound = 16 ounces	1 lb = 16 oz	

1 What is $\frac{1}{2}$ of £1?

2 What is $\frac{1}{2}$ of 1 kilogram?

3 What is $\frac{1}{2}$ of 1 metre?

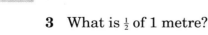

4 What is $\frac{1}{2}$ of a litre?

5 What is $\frac{1}{2}$ of a pound?

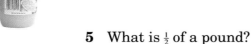

Carrots
38p per lb.

HALVING NUMBERS

 You can use a calculator if it helps. To find half of 56 you press these buttons:

`5` `6` `÷` `2` `=`

1 What is half of 6? Of 16? Of 26? Of … What pattern is there in your answers?

2 What is half of 40? Of 400? Of 4000? Of … What pattern is there in your answers?

3 What is half of 86? Of 186? Of 286? Of …

4 What is half of 34? Of 54? Of 74? Of 94? Of …

5 What is half of 3? Of 5? Of 7? Of 9? Of …

6 What is half of 19? Of 29? Of 39? Of 49? Of …

7 Write down a big number. Find half of it.

Write down a bigger number. Find half of it. Try to make the half of it end in 7.

8 You start with a number. Half of this number is 12. What number did you start with?

9 You start with a number. Half of this number is 17. What number did you start with?

10 What number do you start with if:

(a) half of the number is 36?

(b) half of the number is 62?

(c) half of the number is 193?

11 What is half of half of 36?

Write down some more numbers and find half of half of them.

B4
page
38

12 Half of half of a number is 15. What is the number?

13 How does your calculator show the number $\frac{1}{2}$?

YOU COULD USE:

The computer program called *Take Half* is a film about halving a square.

Watch this computer film. Now draw some halving pictures of your own.

COLOUR HALF

In these pictures half of the square has been coloured.

You will need squared paper for questions 1 and 2.

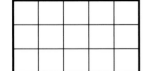

1 Draw several squares like the grid on the right.

Colour half of each of your squares.

Now work with someone else.
Get them to choose one of your squares.
Convince them that exactly half of it has been coloured.

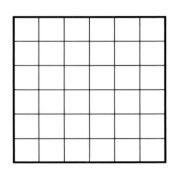

2 Draw several rectangles.
Your rectangles do not have to be this size.
Colour half of each of your rectangles.
You could colour half of other shapes such as those shown below.

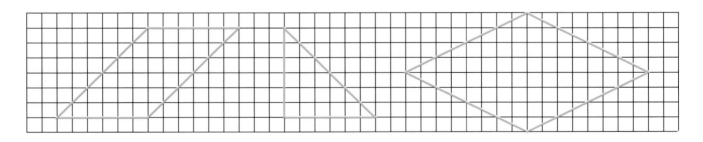

You will need isometric paper for question 3.

3 Draw some shapes on isometric paper.
Colour half of each of your shapes.

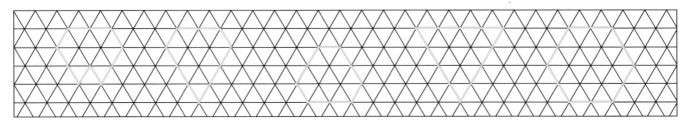

5 BAGS OF CUBES

IDENTICAL BAGS

You could use cubes and bags for this activity.

Or you could imagine what is happening.

1 (*a*) Get 12 red cubes, 8 yellow cubes and two bags.

Put the cubes in the bags. Each bag is to have exactly the same cubes.

What is in each bag?

(*b*) Make up some more problems like this. Give them to someone else to solve.

2 (*a*) Get 24 cubes. Each cube should be either blue or green.

Put the cubes into three bags, so that each bag has exactly the same cubes.

What is in one of your bags?

Compare your answer with other people's answers.

(*b*) Make up some more problems like this. Give them to someone else to answer. You do not need to have two colours. Or three bags. Or 24 cubes.

HOW MANY CUBES ALTOGETHER?

1 There are two bags. One bag contains 7 red cubes and the other contains 17 blue cubes.

How many cubes altogether?

2 There are two bags. One of the bags contains 7 cubes.
One bag contains two *more* cubes than the other bag.

How many cubes altogether?

3 There are two bags. One of the bags contains 8 cubes.
One bag contains twice as many cubes as the other bag. How many cubes altogether?

4 There are three bags. There are 6 cubes in one of the bags.
Empty the cubes from one of the bags into another bag. One bag now contains no cubes. The other two bags now have the same number of cubes.

How many cubes are there altogether?

5 Make up some more problems like these. Give them to someone else to answer.

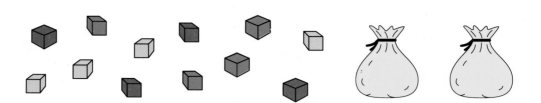

HOW MANY CUBES IN EACH BAG?

1 Get 12 cubes. Put them in two bags.
Each bag is to have the same number of cubes. How many in each bag?

2 Get 12 cubes. Put them in two bags.
One bag is to contain 2 more cubes than the other bag.

3 Get 12 cubes. Put them in two bags.
One bag is to contain twice as many cubes as the other bag.

4 Get 12 cubes. Put them in two bags.
The number of cubes in one of the bags is to be a square number.

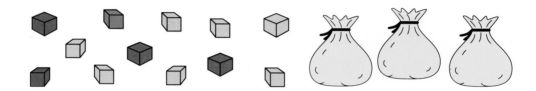

5 Get 12 cubes. Put them in three bags.
The bag with most cubes is to have 4 cubes more than the bag with the smallest number of cubes.

6 Get 12 cubes. Put them in three bags.
The bag with most cubes is to have twice as many cubes as the bag with the smallest number of cubes.

7 Get 12 cubes. Put them in four bags.
Each bag is to have a different number of cubes.

8 Get 12 cubes. Put them in four bags.
Three of the bags are to have the same number of cubes.

9 Make up some more problems like these. Give them to someone else to answer.

B4
page
38

WITHOUT LOOKING

1 (*a*) What colour is the cube that is taken out? Could it be red? Could it be blue?

(*b*) Is the cube more likely to be red, or more likely to be blue?

2 Think about each of the following four situations. Discuss them with other people. You could act them out for yourself.

(*a*)

(*b*)

(c)

(d)

3 (a) A bag contains two red cubes and a yellow cube.

Someone takes a cube out of the bag without looking. She then looks at it and puts it back in the bag. She does this twelve times.

How many times would you expect her to get a red cube? Are you sure?

(b) Do the experiment yourself. Compare what you get with what other people get when they do the experiment.

(c) Make up some other experiments. Predict what you think will happen. Try them out. Give them to other people to do. Compare the answers you get.

PROBABILITIES

>
>
> **I** There is a red cube and a blue cube in a bag. You take one cube without looking. The probability that you get a red cube is $\frac{1}{2}$. This is because
>
> - there is 1 red cube
> - there are 2 cubes altogether.

1 (*a*) A bag contains two red cubes and one blue cube. You take one out without looking.

What is the probability that you get a red cube? What is the probability that you get a blue cube?

(*b*) Make up some more problems like this and solve them. Give them to someone else to solve. Discuss your answers.

2 A bag contains one red cube and one blue cube. The probability of taking out a red cube without looking is $\frac{1}{2}$.

You take a cube out. You then put it back. You do this ten times.

(*a*) How many times might you expect to get a red cube?

(*b*) You do the experiment again. But you do it 16 times. How many times might you expect to get a red cube?

(*c*) You now do the experiment 25 times. How many times might you expect to get a red cube?

(*d*) Make up some more problems like this and solve them.

WHAT WILL YOU GET NEXT?

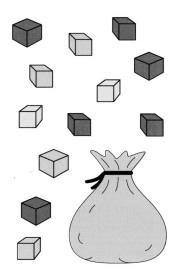

1 Here is a game you can play with several people. You could play it with the whole class.

Put twelve cubes into a bag. Six of the cubes should be red, four blue and two yellow.

Choose a way of recording what is in the bag. You could use a table like this.

	1st	2nd	3rd	4th	etc.
Red	6	6			
Blue	4	3			
Yellow	2	2			
Prediction	Red				
Cube taken	Blue				

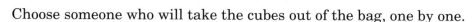

Choose someone who will take the cubes out of the bag, one by one.

- This should be done without looking.
- The cubes taken out should *not* be put back in the bag.
- Just before each cube is taken out of the bag, the players all predict what colour the cube will be.
- When the cube is taken out, you check to see if your prediction is correct.
- You now record what is left in the bag.
- Predict before each of the twelve cubes is taken out of the bag.

When the bag is empty count how many of your predictions were correct.

Play the game more than once. See if you can get better at predicting.

2 Change the game by changing what you put in the bag to start with.

WHAT IS IN THE BAG?

1 Here is another game.

Someone secretly puts 20 cubes into a bag.

- Each cube should be red or blue.
- The person filling the bag should *not* say how many of each colour are used.
- No-one else is allowed to look in the bag.

(*a*) Get someone to take a cube out, without looking.
Record whether it is a red cube or a blue cube.
Put the cube back in the bag.
Repeat this five times.

Now predict how many red cubes are in the bag, and how many blue cubes are in the bag.

(*b*) Get someone to take another cube out without looking.
Record whether it is a red cube or a blue cube.
Put the cube back in the bag.
Repeat this another five times.

Now change your prediction if you want to.

(*c*) Repeat another five times.

(*d*) Can you ever be certain what is in the bag?

Now empty the bag so that people can see how good their predictions were.

(*e*) Play this game several times.

2 Here are some ways of making the game a bit different.

- Change the number of cubes you put into the bag.
- Use three colours instead of two.
- Leave it to the person who fills the bag to decide how many different colours to use. This person also *must not* tell you what these colours are.

B5
page
38

6 SLOT MACHINES

HOT DRINKS MACHINE

1 Write down several different ways of putting the correct money into this machine.

2 What is the smallest number of coins you could use?

3 What is the largest number of coins you could use?

4 Helen says she used 7 coins. What coins could she have used? Is there more than one answer?

5 Ben says he used 15 coins. What coins could he have used? Is there more than one answer?

6 Three people said they used 10 coins. But none of them used the same set of coins. Is this possible?

'I used ten coins.'

'I used ten coins too. But I didn't use the same coins as you.'

'I used ten coins too. But I didn't use the same coins as either of you.'

7 Three people said they used 12 coins. None of them used the same set of coins. Is this possible?

8 Four people said they used the same number of coins. None of them used the same set of coins. Is this possible?

9 Five people said they used the same number of coins. None of them used the same set of coins. Is this possible?

UNDERGROUND TICKETS

Some Underground ticket machine gives change. You do not have to put in the exact amount. If you put in too much the machine gives you change.

The machine takes these coins.

1 You want to buy a 30p ticket. In how many different ways could you put in the exact amount?

2 (*a*) Kalvinder wants to buy a 30p ticket. The money she has is shown in A.

A

B

She puts in the pound coin and gets 70p change.

Dave also wants to buy a 30p ticket. The money he has is shown in B.

What does he put in? How much change does he get?

(*b*) Make up your own problems about people buying 30p tickets. What does each person put in? How much change do they get?

3 The machine sells tickets for the following prices: 30p, 50p, 65p, 85p. The machine is programmed to give change using as few coins as possible.

Here are two ways of getting on 85p ticket:

(*a*) Show two ways of getting a 50p ticket. What change do you get in each case?

(*b*) Show two ways of getting a 65p ticket. What change do you get in each case?

B6
page
39

(*c*) What is the largest number of coins the machine will give as change?

PAY AND DISPLAY

You will need the resource sheet *'Pay and display'*.

 30 days have September,
April, June and November.
All the rest have 31,
Excepting February alone,
Which hath but 28 days clear,
And 29 each leap year.

Some car parks are 'Pay and Display'. You have to buy a ticket from a machine when you park your car. This ticket is displayed on the car windscreen.

In one car park this notice is displayed on the ticket machine.

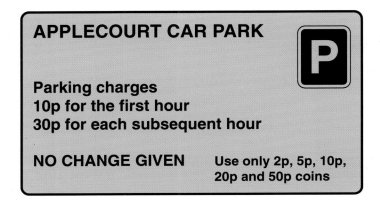

APPLECOURT CAR PARK **P**

Parking charges
10p for the first hour
30p for each subsequent hour

NO CHANGE GIVEN   Use only 2p, 5p, 10p,
                          20p and 50p coins

If you put money in and then press the button it prints a ticket. The time on the ticket is when your car must leave the car park. The ticket looks like this.

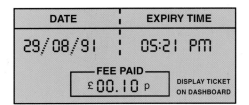

DATE	EXPIRY TIME
29/08/91	05:21 PM

FEE PAID
£00.10 p   DISPLAY TICKET
              ON DASHBOARD

1 The number 239 is used as a check of the date. Explain how.

2 Sue arrived at ten o'clock in the morning on 30th March. She put 10p in the machine and pressed the button.

   What did the ticket say? Show this on the resource sheet.

3 Jilesh arrived 10 minutes later, put in 70p and pressed the button. What did his ticket say?

4 The following day Andrew arrived at half past two in the afternoon. He put in 40p. What did his ticket say?

5 Three quarters of an hour later Sharon put in 70p and pressed the button. What did her ticket say?

6 The next day Mary arrived at the car park at a quarter to ten in the morning.

How much money did Mary put in? What did her ticket say?

7 Two weeks later Otis arrived at five to twelve in the morning and put in 40p. What did his ticket say?

8 Make up your own questions about people using the car park and the tickets they got. Give them to someone else to solve.

9 Sometimes the machine goes wrong. It misses out some of the printing on the tickets. Here are some of the faulty tickets it has produced.

(a)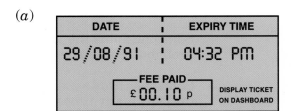

(c)

(b)

(d)

Use the resource sheet to show what each ticket should say.

B7
page
39

10 Make up your own faulty tickets and give them to someone else to solve.

REVIEW EXERCISES B

EXERCISE 4 Number 2

1 Copy each blue picture. Put equal numbers in the corners.

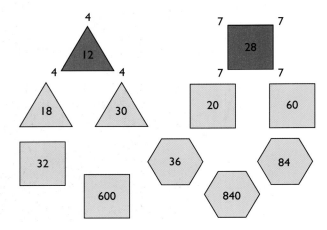

2 When two numbers are added together the answer is 20.
When the numbers are multiplied together the answer ends in 1.
When one number is subtracted from the other the answer is less than 10.
What are the two numbers?

3 Find *half* of each of these numbers:

6, 20, 14, 36, 100, 1000, 254, 1336, 365.

4 Find a *quarter* of each of these numbers:

8, 20, 44, 100, 1000, 500, 360, 256, 1336, 366.

5 (a) How many millimetres is half a centimetre?
(b) How many grams is half a kilogram?
(c) How many seconds is half a minute?
(d) How many hours is half a day?
(e) How many ounces is half a pound?
(f) How many centimetres is a quarter of a metre?
(g) How many minutes is a quarter of an hour?
(h) How many grams is a quarter of a kilogram?

6 In these sequences each number is half of the number before it. Find the next three numbers in each sequence:

(a) $1, \frac{1}{2}, \frac{1}{4}, \ldots$
(b) $6, 3, 1.5, \ldots$
(c) $1000, 500, 250, \ldots$

EXERCISE 5 Probability

1 Arrange these statements in order. Start with the least likely and finish with the most likely.

A Tomorrow it will rain.
B Tomorrow you will be struck by lightning.
C Tomorrow you will be eaten by a unicorn.
D Tomorrow you will eat some food.
E Tomorrow you will have toothache.
F Tomorrow someone will smile at you.

2 In a family there are three boys and a girl. They take it in turns to wash up. Someone visits the family. What is the probability that a boy will be washing up that day?

3

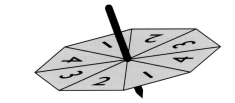

Someone spins the spinner. What is the probability that she gets a 3?

4 Someone throws a dice 30 times.
(a) How many times would you expect them to get a 5?
(b) How many times would you expect them to get an even number?
(c) How many times would you expect them to get a number bigger than 4?

5 In class 7H there are 12 girls and 18 boys. In class 8K there are 10 girls and 16 boys. A child is picked at random from each class. Which child is more likely to be a girl?

EXERCISE 6 Money

Do not use a calculator until you have to.

1 You have these coins.

How much money do you have?

2 Andy has two coins and Steve has one coin. Both have the same amount of money.

How much money do they have?
(There is more than one possible answer.)

3 Mehreen has three coins and Fatima has one coin. Both have the same amount of money.

How much money do they have?
(There is more than one possible answer.)

4 Raffle tickets cost 20p each. How many do you have to sell to collect £5?

5

**BURGERS
86p**

Jim buys three burgers. How much change does he get from a ten pound note?

6 John likes Toffoes, which cost 23p each. He goes to the shop with £1. How many Toffoes can he buy and what change does he get?

EXERCISE 7 Time

1 How long is it before the train leaves?

**VICTORIA STATION
LONDON**

DOVER EXPRESS DEPART 10.35
BROMLEY SOUTH
CHATHAM
CANTERBURY
DOVER

2

**NEW STREET STATION
BIRMINGHAM**

PRESTON DEPART 9.15
STOKE ON TRENT
MANCHESTER
BOLTON
PRESTON

It takes $1\frac{1}{2}$ hours from Birmingham to Preston.
When does the train get to Preston?

3

London	15.30
Gadstown	17.10

Here is part of a train timetable.

How long does the journey take?

4

HOLIDAYS			
Name	**Start date**	**Length**	**Finish date**
Meena	13th July	1 week	?
Rachel	9th May	2 weeks	?
Donna	20th June	2 weeks	?
Paul	22nd August	3 weeks	?

What is the finish date of each holiday?

7 LEAVES

This task is about leaves.

You need to collect some leaves.

You need about twelve leaves of different shapes and types for the first two activities.

You also need several leaves of just two types for later activities: for example, several oak leaves and several ivy leaves.

If it is not possible to collect leaves you can use the resource sheets 'Leaves 1' and 'Leaves 2'.

HOW BIG IS A LEAF?

 Some leaves are easy to compare. The ivy leaf can be covered up by the sycamore leaf. So, the sycamore leaf is definitely bigger.

Other leaves are harder to compare.

1   Choose about twelve of the leaves you have collected. Alternatively, use the resource sheet 'Leaves 1'.

Try to arrange your leaves in order of size, just by looking at them.

Write down your order, starting with the biggest.

Here is a way of finding out whether one leaf is bigger than another. Cover both of the leaves with counters.

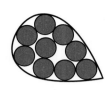

Ivy   Privet

Decide whether the counters are allowed to overlap the edges of the leaves or not.

2 (*a*) How many counters are needed to cover each of your leaves?

(*b*) Make a new list of your leaves in order of size. Start with the biggest.

For question 3 you need a piece of centimetre-squared paper.

3 (*a*) If you are using the leaves on the resource sheet you need to cut them out.

Choose three leaves. Lay each leaf on centimetre-squared paper and draw round it.

(*b*) Count the number of squares for each leaf.

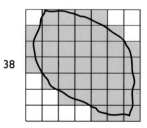

38

 There are several ways of counting.

You could count the squares needed to cover the leaf completely. This *overestimates* the size of the leaf.

You could count only the squares which fit inside the leaf completely. This *underestimates* the size of the leaf.

You could count the squares which are more than half inside the leaf. This gives a *better estimate*, but you do not know whether it is too big or too small.

19

The area of a leaf means the amount of space it covers. One way of measuring area is in square centimetres.

Suppose a leaf needs 28 centimetre squares.

Then the area of the leaf is 28 square centimetres. You can write it like this.

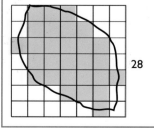

28

The area of the leaf is 28 cm^2.

(*c*) What is the area of each of the leaves you have measured?

BEING MORE ACCURATE

For this activity you need a piece of millimetre-squared paper.

1 (*a*) Use the same three leaves as for question 3 on page 41.

Lay each leaf on millimetre-squared paper and draw round it.

(*b*) Count the number of squares for each leaf. (You might need to invent quick ways to do this.)

 Suppose a leaf needs 612 millimetre squares.

Then the area of the leaf is 612 square millimetres. You can write it like this.

The area of the leaf is 612 mm².

(*c*) What is the area (in square millimetres) of each of the leaves you have measured?

   100 square millimetres are the same size as 1 square centimetre.

I cm²   100 mm²

612 square millimetres are the same size as 6.12 square centimetres.

(*d*) Change your answers to (*c*), so that they give the area of each leaf in square centimetres.

2 Compare your answers to question 1(*d*) with your answers to question 3(*c*) on page 41.

C8
page
52

Which answers do you think are more accurate? Explain why.

WHICH TREE HAS THE BIGGER LEAVES?

You need centimetre-squared paper or millimetre-squared paper for this activity.

For this activity use two types of leaves which you have collected. Or else use the resource sheet '*Leaves 2*'.

'Are oak leaves bigger than ivy leaves?'

'Some oak leaves are bigger than some ivy leaves.'

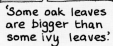
'But some ivy leaves are bigger than some oak leaves.'

'You could find the average size of oak leaves and ivy leaves?'

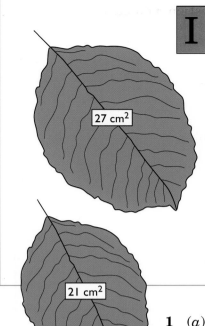

I This is how to find the **mean area** of these six beech leaves.

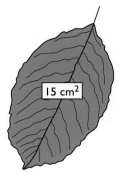

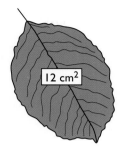

Total area = 6 + 27 + 15 + 21 + 11 + 12 = 92 cm
Mean area = 92 ÷ 6 = 15 cm² (to nearest whole number).

1 (*a*) Find the mean area for each type of leaf.

(*b*) Which type of leaf is bigger, if you judge by using the mean area?

I This is how to find the **median area** of these six beech leaves.

The six areas in order of size are:

6, 11, 12, 15, 21, 27.

The middle two areas are 12 and 15.

The median area is 27 ÷ 2 = 13.5 cm².

2 (*a*) Find the median area for each of your types of leaf.

(*b*) Which type of leaf is bigger, if you judge by using the median area?

3 Is it better to use mean area or median area to compare the two types of leaf? Explain your answer.

HOW MUCH DO LEAVES VARY?

Some plants have leaves which vary a lot in size.

Other plants have leaves which are all more or less the same size.

1 Devise a method of deciding which of your two types of leaf varies most in size.

A3
page
23

8 WHAT IS A SQUARE?

ALL SQUARE

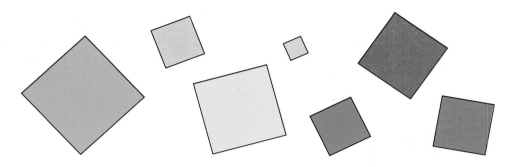

What is it about these shapes that makes them all squares?

FOLDING A SQUARE

Take a sheet of paper. Fold it and cut it to produce a square of paper.

Now fold the square in half. What shape do you get? Does it depend on how you fold it?

Fold it in half again. What shape do you get now?

Draw pictures to show what shapes you get when you keep folding a square in half.

LOGO SQUARES

1 Use *Logo* to draw a square.

   Now draw a square which is $\frac{1}{4}$ of the area of the first square. Explain how you know it is $\frac{1}{4}$ of the area.

2 Use *Logo* to draw squares inside each other, like (*a*) or like (*b*).

(*a*)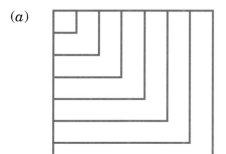

(*b*)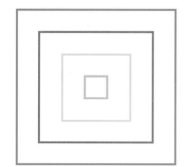

COORDINATE SQUARES

 Look at the red square in figure 1.

The coordinates of its corners are (3,4), (6,4), (6,7) and (3,7).

Look at the blue square.

The coordinates of its corners are (2,0), (4,2), (2,4) and (0,2).

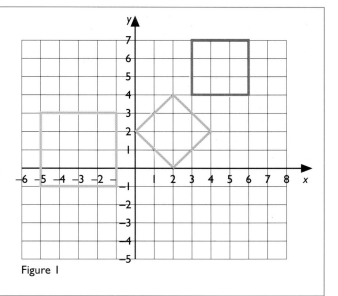

Figure 1

1 (a) Draw axes on a sheet of squared paper.

(b) Draw some squares on your axes.

Write down the coordinates of the corners of your squares.

 Look at the green square in figure 1. Its coordinates are (−5, −1), (−1, −1), (−1, 3) and (−5, 3).

2 Draw some more squares.

Write down the coordinates of the corners of your squares.

> You might want to draw some new axes for question 3.

3 (a) Three of the corners of a square are at (0,3), (2,5) and (0,5).

Where is the fourth corner?

(b) Three of the corners of a square are at (6,3), (6,7) and (8,5). Where is the fourth corner?

4 Where is the fourth corner of a square if three of the corners are at

(a) (2,2), (−2,−2) and (−2,2)?

(b) (5,0), (0,5) and (0,−5)?

(c) (3,3), (6,4) and (2,6)?

5 There is more than one answer to each part of this question.

Where are the other two corners of a square, if two of the corners are at

(a) (4,2) and (8,2)?

(b) (−1,2) and (−1,5)?

(c) (2,1) and (3,6)?

C9
page
52

OVERLAPPING SQUARES

For this activity you need a sheet of plain paper and a sheet of tracing paper (or an acetate sheet).

If you have two squares you can overlap them.

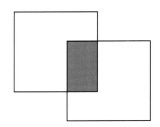 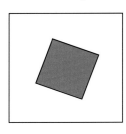 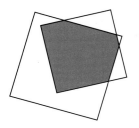

In each picture the *overlap* has been coloured *red*.

The squares might be the same size, or they might be different sizes.

1 Draw a square on the plain paper and another square on the tracing paper (or acetate sheet).

This will help you see what shapes you can get as overlaps.

Sketch your own pictures of two squares overlapping.

2 Which of the angles in your pictures look the same size?

Show which angles you think are the same by colouring them.

3 What different shapes can you make by overlapping two squares?

Can any of these shapes be made?

You might find the resource sheet *'Shapes'* helpful.

Rectangle
Rhombus
Isosceles triangle
Pentagon
Hexagon
Octagon
Decagon
Kite
Trapezium

If you are sure that a shape *cannot* be made, try to explain why.

4 What shapes can be made by overlapping *three* squares?

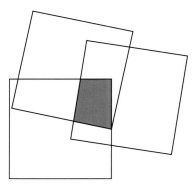 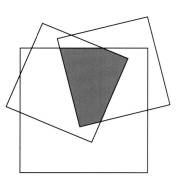

CUTTING THE CORNERS OFF A SQUARE

The picture below shows the corners cut from a square. In the picture all the cut corners are the *same* size and all the cuts are symmetrical across the corner.

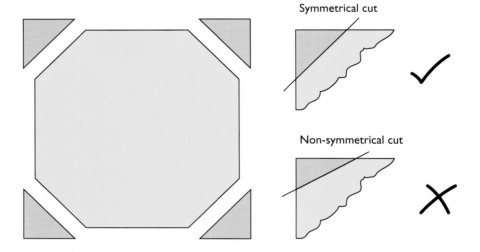

Symmetrical cut ✓

Non-symmetrical cut ✗

1 The corners are cut off as shown above.
What shape is left?

2 The cuts are made bigger, so that they meet.
What shape is left now?

3 The cuts are made even bigger, so that they overlap.
What shape is left?

4 Some of the corners are cut, but not all of them, like A below.
What shapes can be left?

5 More is cut from some corners than from others.
What shapes can be left?

6 Suppose now that the cuts are *not* symmetrical across the corners, like B below.
What shapes can be left?

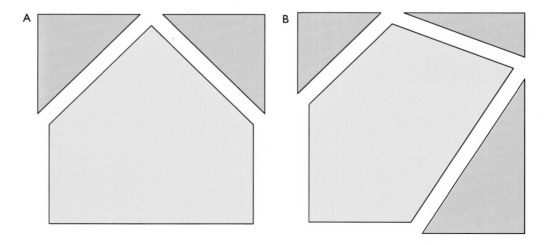

A

B

9 A SLICE OF PIE

CUTTING UP PIES

Get the resource sheet 'Pies'.

1 On the resource sheet '*Pies*' there are eight pieces of pie.

   (*a*) Which piece do you think is the biggest?

   (*b*) Which piece of pie do you think is the smallest?

2 (*a*) Cut out the pieces of pie.

   (*b*) Find the pieces called A and B.

   Which of them is bigger?

   (*c*) Arrange all the pieces in order of size. Write down a list of letters to show the order.

3 You should have eight pieces of pie.

   (*a*) Make two pies out of the pieces.

   Which pieces are in each pie?

   (*b*) Now make two pies in a different way.

   Which pieces are in each pie this time?

You need a protractor for question 4.

4 (*a*) Measure the angle of piece A with a protractor.

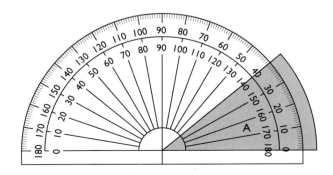

You should find that the angle is 40°.

(b) Measure the angle of piece B with a protractor.

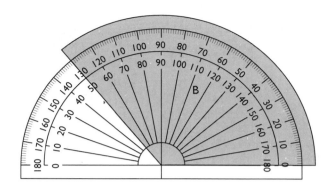

You should find that the angle is 130°.

(c) Measure the angles of the other pieces.

5 (a) Find the total of the angles of *all* the pieces.

(b) In question 3 you made four different pies.
Find the total of the angles in *one* pie.
Do this for each of the four pies.

TWO MORE PIES

1 Here are eight pieces of pie.

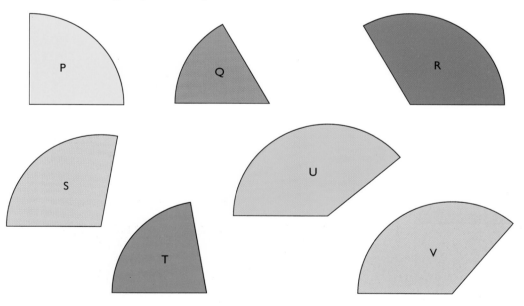

(a) Which piece do you think is the biggest?

(b) Which piece of pie do you think is the smallest?

You need a protractor for question 2.

2 Measure the angle of each of the pieces with a protractor.

3 Find the total of the angles of *all* the pieces.

4 The eight pieces can be used to make two complete pies. Which pieces go in each pie?

FAIR SHARES

You need a protractor for this activity.

1 Some people share a pie.
They all have the same amount of pie.

Each one has a piece like A.

(a) Measure the angle of the piece of pie.

(b) How many people shared the pie?

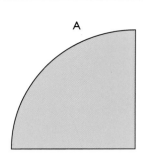
A

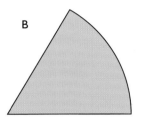
B

2 Some other people share a different pie.
Each one has a piece like B.

(a) Measure the angle of the piece of pie.

(b) How many people shared the pie?

3 How many people share a pie equally, if each of them gets a piece like C?

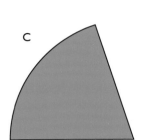
C

4 Three people share a pie.
Each of them has a piece of the same size.
Draw a picture of one of the pieces. Use a protractor, so that the angle is accurate.

5 Eight people share a pie.
Each of them has a piece of the same size.
Draw a picture of one of the pieces.

PIE CHARTS

You need a protractor for this activity.

Pie charts are used to show the results of surveys.

1 Some people were asked which TV channel they watched most.
Here are the results of the survey.

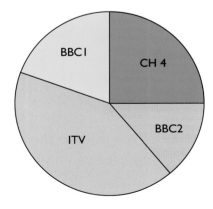

(a) Which channel was most popular?
(b) Which channel was least popular?
(c) Which channel was watched most by exactly a quarter of the people?

2 Some people were asked which was their favourite pet. Here are the results.

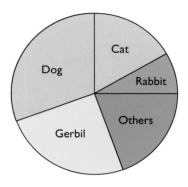

(a) Which was the favourite pet?

(b) Which was the second favourite?

(c) Did more than a third of the people say that a dog was their favourite pet?

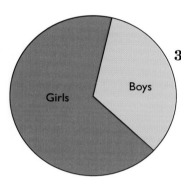

3 This pie chart shows 30 children who went to the theatre.

(a) What is the angle of the boys' piece?

(b) How many boys went?

(c) What is the angle of the girls' piece?

4 40 people were asked which paper they read. Here are the results.

(a) How many people read the Sun?

(b) How many people read Today?

(c) How many people did not read a paper?

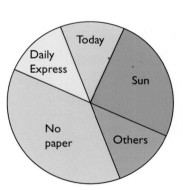

5 12 people were asked to name their favourite colour. Here are the results.

Favourite colour	Number of people
Red	4
Blue	3
Yellow	3
Green	2

C10
page
53

Draw a pie chart to show these results.

REVIEW EXERCISES C

EXERCISE 8 Area

1 Find the approximate area of each of these shapes.

(a)

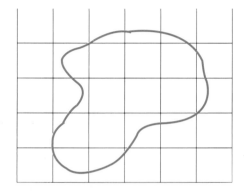

(b)

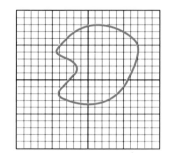

2 Some people want to know the area of this shape.

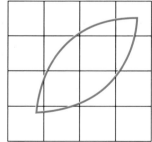

Here are some statements they make.
A The area is bigger than 3 cm².
B The area is less than 5 cm².
C The area is bigger than 7 cm².
D The area is almost exactly 5 cm².
E The area is between 4 cm² and 6 cm².

(a) Which statements are *certainly* true?
(b) Which statements are *certainly* false?
(c) Which statements are *probably* true?

(d) Which statements *could* be true?

3 Jane estimates the area of a shape and says it is 1263 mm².
Ann says this is a silly answer, because you cannot count that accurately. She says she will give the answer to the nearest square centimetre. What answer does Ann give?

4 The area of a leaf is about 8.5 cm².
(a) What is the approximate area of the leaf in square millimetres?
(b) John estimates that a tree has 1000 leaves of this kind. Estimate the total area of the tree's leaves. Give your answer
(i) in square centimetres.
(ii) in square metres.

EXERCISE 9 Coordinates and shapes

1 Write down the coordinates of the points P, Q, R and S.

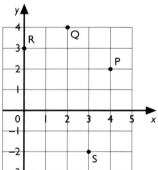

You can use squared paper for questions 2 and 3.

2 (a) Plot each set of coordinates. Join them up in order.
The first has been done for you.

(i) (1, 2), (5, 2), (6, 4), (2, 4).

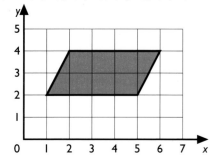

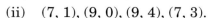

(ii)   (7, 1), (9, 0), (9, 4), (7, 3).
(iii)   (10, 4), (12, 3), (14, 4), (12, 5).
(iv)   (9, 6), (11, 7), (10, 9), (8, 8).
(v)   (1, 9), (3, 7), (4, 8), (2, 10).

(b) Name each of the shapes you have
drawn using one of these words.

Square
Rectangle
Parallelogram
Trapezium
Rhombus

3   In each of the following, three corners of a
rectangle are given. Find the coordinates of
the fourth corner.

(a) (2, 2), (4, 2), (4, 5).
(b) (−3, 3), (1, 3), (1, 4).
(c) (0, 5), (2, 7), (1, 8).
(d) (−3, −2), (−1, −3), (1, 1).
(e) (5, 0), (7, 2), (6.5, 2.5).

EXERCISE 10 Angles

You will need a protractor for this exercise.

1
Get the resource sheet 'Measuring angles'.

(a) Measure all the angles of the diagrams
on the resource sheet.
Show your answers on the sheet. One
angle is already shown.
(b) Find the total of the three angles in
each of the triangles.
(c) Find the total of the four angles in each
of the quadrilaterals.
(d) One triangle has two of its angles equal.
Measure the sides of this triangle.
Write down what you notice.
(e) Which shape is a parallelogram?
What can you say about the angles of
this parallelogram?
(f) In which shapes are two of the sides
parallel?

You can use isometric paper or squared paper for
questions 2, 3, 4 and 5.

2   (a) Draw a triangle which has all three
angles equal.
(b) Draw a triangle which has two angles
equal.
(c) Draw a triangle which has none of its
angles equal.

3   Draw a parallelogram. Measure its angles.
What do you notice.

4   Draw a quadrilateral which has just two of
its angles equal.

5   (a) Draw a triangle which has one angle
which is bigger than a right-angle.
(b) Can a triangle have two angles which
are bigger than a right-angle?

6   36 people were asked what their favourite
sport was. Here are their results.

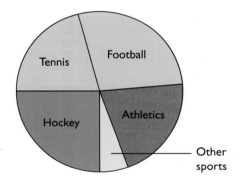

(a) Which was the most popular sport?
(b) How many people said hockey?
(c) Which two sports were equally popular?
(d) The 'Other sports' mentioned were
cycling and swimming.
How many people said swimming?

7   18 people were asked where they came in
their family. Here are the replies:

first child 9,
second child 6,
third child 2,
fourth child 1.

Draw a pie chart to show this information.

10 WORDS

WORD BUILDING

1 How many words can you make from the letters in the word MATHEMATICS?

Do not use any letter more than once, unless it is in MATHEMATICS more than once.

2 How many words can you make from the letters in the word MATHS?

3 How many words can you make from the letters in the word STARE?

4 How many words can you make from the letters in the word FOXED?

5 What makes STARE easier to use than FOXED? Discuss this with other people.

VOWELS AND CONSONANTS

I There are 26 letters in the English alphabet. 5 of them are vowels and 21 are consonants.

To find the percentage of letters which are vowels:

- divide 5 by 26;
- then multiply by 100.

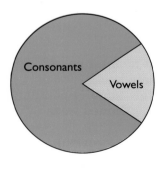

1 What percentage of letters are vowels?

2 What percentage of letters are consonants?

3 (a) Choose a book and choose a page from this book. Count the number of vowels in the first 100 letters on the page you have chosen.

(b) What percentage of the first 100 letters are vowels? What percentage are consonants?

4 (a) Count the number of vowels in the first 200 letters on the same page.

(b) What percentage of the first 200 letters are vowels? What percentage are consonants?

5 Compare your answers to questions 1, 2, 3 and 4. Comment on what you notice.

6 Compare your answers to all the questions with the answers obtained by other people.

Are all the answers the same? Would you expect them to be?

FIRST LETTERS

What letters do words start with?

Every letter of the alphabet is the first letter of some word, but some letters are used much more often than others.

Which letter do you guess is used most as the first letter of a word?

1 (a) Choose a book and choose a page from this book. Write down the letters which the first 100 words start with.

You could record your results like this.

A	⊤⊦⊦ ⊤⊦⊦	H	I	O	⊤⊦⊦ ⊤⊦⊦ III	V	
B	I	I	IIII	P	⊤⊦⊦ ⊤⊦⊦ I	W	II
C	⊤⊦⊦	J		Q		X	
D	I	K		R	⊤⊦⊦	Y	II
E	III	L	⊤⊦⊦ ⊤⊦⊦	S	III	Z	
F	I	M	⊤⊦⊦ II	T	⊤⊦⊦ ⊤⊦⊦ ⊤⊦⊦ I		
G		N	I	U	IIII		

(b) Which are the three most common starting letters for the words you counted?

(c) What percentage of the words you counted start with each of these three letters?

2 Get a dictionary.

Use the dictionary to find the commonest starting letters for words.

You could count all the words that begin with A, all the words that begin with B, and so on.
But you might find it easier to find how many pages there are of words beginning with A, beginning with B, and so on.

(a) Which are the three most common starting letters in the dictionary?

(b) What percentage of words start with each of these letters?

3 (a) List the first letters of the surnames of all the people in your class.

(b) Which are the three most common letters?

(c) What percentage of names start with each of these letters?

4 (a) List the first letters of the first names of all the people in your class.

(b) Which are the three most common letters?

(c) What percentage of names start with each of these letters?

D11
page
68

5 Compare your answers to questions 1, 2, 3 and 4 above.
Are you surprised?

LENGTH OF WORDS

How long are English words? They are different lengths of course, but which length is the most common?

1 (a) Choose a book and choose a page from this book. Record the lengths of the first 100 words on the page.

You could record your results like this

1	/	6	THL //	11	///
2	THL THL THL ///	7	THL ///	12	
3	THL THL THL THL THL	8	THL THL	13	/
4	THL THL	9	THL	14	
5	THL	10	THL //	15	

(b) Which are the three most common lengths for words on the page?

  To find the **mean** length of 100 words:

first find the total number of letters in these words, then divide by 100 (because there are 100 words).

(c) Find the *mean* length of the 100 words you counted.

2 Get a dictionary.

(a) Choose a page of the dictionary.

Record the lengths of the first 100 words listed, starting with the words on the chosen page.

(b) Which are the three most common lengths for words?

(c) Find the *mean* length of these 100 words.

(d) Compare your answers with those of other people in your class.

3 Compare your answers to questions 1 and 2.

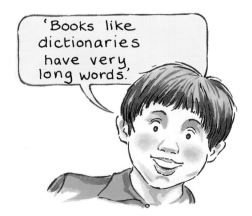

'Books like dictionaries have very long words.'

ROAD NAMES AND HOUSE NUMBERS

1 (*a*) What is the name of your road?

(*b*) Your road name might have several different words.

How many letters altogether are there in your road name?

(*c*) Collect results for the whole class.

(*d*) What is the mean number of letters in the road names of people in your class?

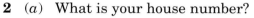

2 (*a*) What is your house number?

(*b*) Collect the house numbers of all people in your class.

(*c*) Group the results together like this:

> You might have to decide what to do if some people's houses do not have numbers.

House number	Tally	Total
1–10		
11–20		
21–30		
31–40		
41–50		
51–60		

(*d*) Draw a bar graph to show the house numbers for people in your class.

> You might have to be creative if some people in your class have very large house numbers.

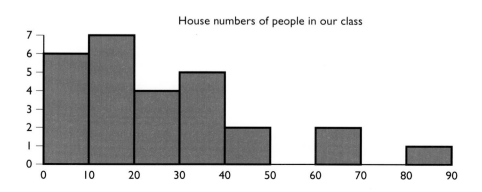

House numbers of people in our class

A3 page 23

11 CUBE MODELS

| You will need interlocking cubes for all these activities. |

Here is a model made with six interlocking cubes.

The cubes are joined so that their faces match exactly.

TALKING ABOUT YOUR MODEL

Work with a partner for this activity.

Make a model from six interlocking cubes. Do not let your partner see it.

Describe your model to your partner. Your partner must try to make an identical model.

You can use whatever words you like to describe your model. But do not write anything down.

DRAWING YOUR MODELS

You will need isometric dot paper for this activity.

This is how you could draw the model at the top of this page.

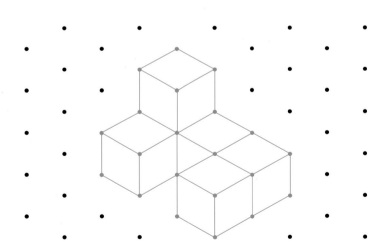

Draw your model on the paper.
Draw your partner's model.

MIRROR IMAGES

Imagine that your model is looking at itself in a mirror. What does it see?

1   Make a model which is the mirror image of your model.

With some models, when you make the mirror image model it is exactly the same model. Is this true for your model?

2   Make some more models with six cubes. Make their mirror images. You might want to draw what you make.

HOW MANY MODELS?

1   If all your class are working on this task, everyone will have drawn some models made from six cubes.

(a)   How many models have been drawn altogether?

(b)   How many of these models are *different*?

2   Make several different models from six cubes. How many *different* models are there in the classroom now?

Try to think of a model which nobody has made.

Working together, your class could try to make all possible models from six cubes.

Keep the models that have been made. You will need them for other activities.

HOW MUCH PAINT?

Suppose everyone in the class painted the outside of their six-cube model.

Which models would need the most paint? Which models would need the least paint?

Answer the same questions about models made from a different number of cubes.

HOW TALL IS YOUR MODEL?

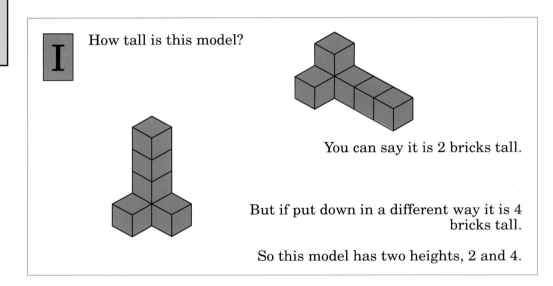

I How tall is this model?

You can say it is 2 bricks tall.

But if put down in a different way it is 4 bricks tall.

So this model has two heights, 2 and 4.

1 Make a model from six cubes. What heights does it have?

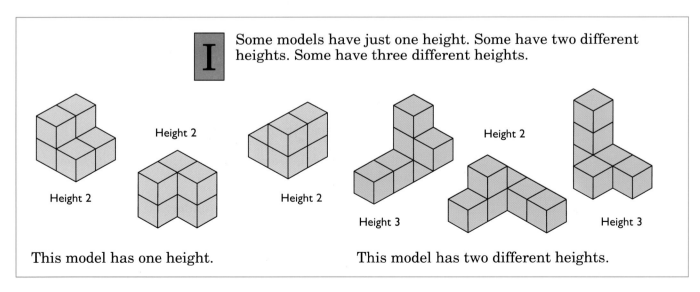

I Some models have just one height. Some have two different heights. Some have three different heights.

Height 2

Height 2

Height 2

Height 2

Height 3

Height 3

This model has one height.

This model has two different heights.

D12
page
68

2 Investigate the different possible heights for models made from six cubes.

3 What about models made from a different number of cubes?

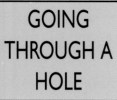

GOING THROUGH A HOLE

This model will go through this hole if it goes this way.

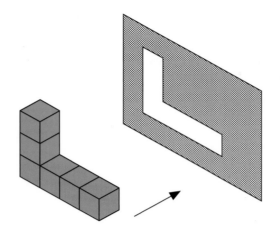

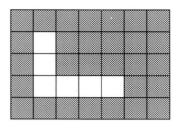

But it will go through a smaller hole if it goes this way.

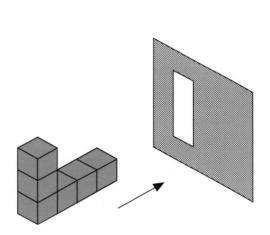

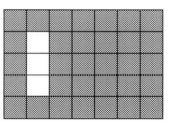

It will, of course, go through this hole because this hole is bigger.

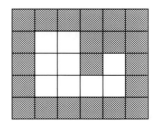

1 Find a hole which *all* models made of six cubes will go through.

Now try to find the *smallest* hole which you think *all* models made of six cubes will go through.

F19
page
99

2 Do the same thing for a different number of cubes.

TELLING A COMPUTER ...

I Suppose you wanted to get a computer to draw your model. You would have to tell it where the cubes are.

You might be able to use the computer program *Build*.

With *Build* you start with one cube on the screen.

You tell the computer where to put other cubes by using these commands:

Up, Down, Left, Right, In, Out

You just type U, D, L, R, I or O.

So, if you type UUUUU you would get this:

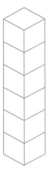

If you type UURRD you would get this:

If you type UURRO you would get this:

Usually if you type five letters you get a model of six cubes. Why? This is not always true, because you might need to go back to a cube, already drawn.

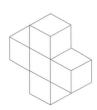

UUDRLL

1 Make a model from six cubes. Describe your model using this method. Now describe someone else's model.

2 Some models made from seven cubes can be described using six letters. Others need more than six letters to describe them. Try to find a model of each sort.

3 Here is a large cube, made of eight cubes.

Describe this model using seven letters. There are lots of different ways of doing this.

127
page
162

Collect together all the different descriptions produced by different people.

Look for patterns in some or all of the descriptions.

GUESS MY MODEL

One person makes a model from four cubes but does not let anyone else see it.

The other person or people have to guess what the model is.

- The model builder does *not* describe the model.
- The guessers have to ask questions.

Work with someone else for this activity. Or the whole class could work together.

You can also play this game with a model made from six cubes. This is quite difficult.

TEAM GAME

Two people secretly build a model from about 20 interlocking cubes.

The rest of the class is divided into teams of three or four. The model is placed where none of the teams can see it.

Each team has a surveyor. The surveyors go to look at the model. They come back and tell their team about the model. The surveyors must not touch any of the cubes. The other members of the team build the model.

The surveyors can go to look at the model as often as they want. No-one else must look at the model.

The winning team is the team whose model is closest to the hidden model.

If you want, you can try to get the colours right as well as the shape.

TWELVE DAYS OF CHRISTMAS

On the first day of Christmas my true love sent to me
A partridge in a pear tree.

On the second day of Christmas my true love sent to me
Two turtle doves
And a partridge in a pear tree.

On the third day of Christmas my true love sent to me
Three French hens
Two turtle doves
And a partridge in a pear tree.

On the fourth day of Christmas my true love sent to me
Four calling birds
Three French hens
Two turtle doves
And a partridge in a pear tree.

On the fifth day of Christmas my true love sent to me
Five gold rings
Four calling birds ...

Six geese a~laying
Seven swans a~swimming
Eight maids a~milking
Nine Lords a~leaping
Ten ladies dancing
Eleven pipers piping
Twelve drummers drumming

The whole of the song has not been printed. It is a long song. It has twelve verses. Perhaps you know the song. If not, the first four verses have been printed in full to show how the verses grow. Before working on the activities you might want to discuss the song with other people. You might want to sing it.

HOW MANY PRESENTS?

1 (*a*) How many partridges did the true love give?

   (*b*) How many turtle doves did the true love give?

   (*c*) How many French hens?

2 How many presents did the true love give altogether?

3 What was the total number of legs on all the presents? You might need to think carefully about this.

CHANGING THE RULES

1 The true love promises another set of presents next Christmas.

(a) How many presents would the true love give using this method?

(b) How many presents does the true love give using this method?

(c) Think of other ways of cutting down the presents.

2 How many presents does the true love give?

3 How many presents does he give this year?

CHANGING THE PRESENTS

Next year the true love has lost most of his money. He decides to give some new presents, and only to give them for six days.

On the first day, a puppy.

On the second day, two goldfish and a puppy.

On the third day, three red roses, two goldfish and a puppy.

On the fourth day, four ladybirds, three red roses, two goldfish and a puppy.

On the fifth day, five spiders, four ladybirds, three red roses, two goldfish and a puppy.

On the sixth day, six canaries, five spiders, four ladybirds, three red roses, two goldfish and a puppy.

1 (a) How many presents altogether this year?

  (b) How many eyes altogether?

  (c) How many legs altogether?

2 What order should he give the presents? How many legs will he give? How many eyes?

3 When the presents arrive, there are 180 legs and 92 eyes altogether.

In what order were the presents given?
(There are several possible answers.)

4 Make up your own problem about the presents.

Give it to someone else to solve.

D13 page 69

SING YOUR OWN SONG

Make up your own puzzle written as a song for Christmas.

- It could be like the Twelve Days of Christmas. Or it could be something quite different.

- You might want to use your song to make a puzzle Christmas card.

A Christmas Puzzle
Misha had a piece of cloth which she wanted to cut up to make two perfect squares. Misha cut four pieces out, along the lines that divide the 25 squares of the pattern. When sewn together, the pattern on the smaller squares still matched. There is only one way to do it. Can you work it out?

REVIEW EXERCISES D

EXERCISE 11 **Percentages**

1 Fatima surveyed 100 people. 7 of them were colour blind.

   (*a*) What percentage were colour blind?

   (*b*) What percentage were not colour blind?

2 Some people were asked whether they liked the Beatles. 27% said yes. 48% said no.

   What percentage of people didn't know?

3 There are 500 children in a school. 260 of them are girls.

   What percentage are boys?

4 The attendance at a football match was 20 000. There were 6000 women at the match.

   What percentage of those attending the match were women?

5 There are 57 teachers in a school. 22 of them are men.

   What percentage of the teachers are women?

EXERCISE 12 **Solid shapes 1**

Do not use cubes until you have to.

1 (*a*) Which of these cubes models have mirror symmetry?

A
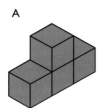
B
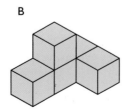
C
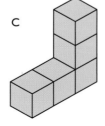

   (*b*) Draw on isometric dot paper the mirror image of each model.

2 Here are some cube models.

A

B
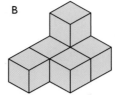
C
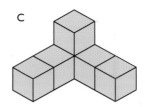

   (*a*) How many cubes are needed for each model?

   (*b*) Which of the models has the biggest surface area? Which has the smallest surface area?

3 Figure 1 shows a cube model.

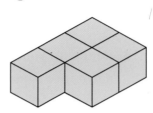

Figure 1
Figure 2

Figure 2 shows a different cube model. It has the same volume *and* the same surface area as the first model.

Find a different cube model for each of these models and draw it.
Each different model should have the same volume and the same surface area as the first model.

A B C D
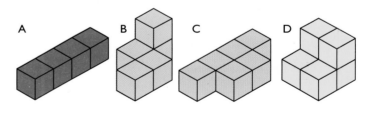

EXERCISE 13 **Number patterns 1**

1 (*a*) Draw the next two shapes in this pattern.

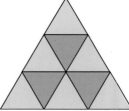

(b) This sequence gives the total number of triangles (pink and blue) in each pattern

1, 4, 9, ...

What are the next two numbers in this sequence?

(c) This sequence gives the number of blue triangles in each pattern

1, 3, 6, ...

What are the next two numbers in this sequence?
What is the 10th number in this sequence?

2 Three different towers can be made with one red cube and two blue cubes.

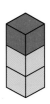 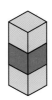 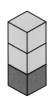

(a) How many different towers can be made from one red cube and three blue cubes?

(b) How many from one red cube and five blue cubes?

(c) How many from one red cube and 100 blue cubes?

(d) How many from one red cube and N blue cubes?

3 Four counters can be separated into two sets in two different ways.

Seven counters can be separated into two sets in three different ways.

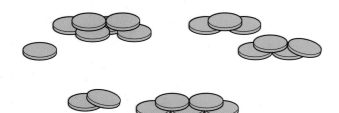

(a) Copy and complete this table

Number of counters	Number of ways
2	
3	
4	2
5	
6	
7	3
8	
9	
10	

(b) In how many ways can 20 counters be separated into two sets?

(c) What about 15 counters? 100? 99?

(d) What about N counters?

4 Balls can be piled in triangular layers like this:

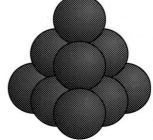

Figure 1

or they can be piled in square layers like this.

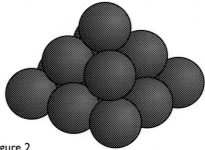

Figure 2

A shop has some balls on display. There is the right number of balls to make a triangular pile, like the one in figure 1. Someone sells one ball. There is now exactly the right number of balls left to make a square pile, like the one in figure 2.

How many balls were in the triangular pile?

13 THE ANSWER IS 42

The answer is 42. What is the question?

There are a lot of possible questions – an infinite number, in fact.

Here are a few.

What is 41 + 1?   What is 52 – 10?
What is 40 + 2?   What is 62 – 20?
What is 39 + 3?   What is …
What is …

What is 2 + 40?   What is 7 × 6?
What is 12 + 30?   What is …
What is 22 + 20?
What is …

What is 420 ÷ 10?   What is 4.2 × 10?
What is …   What is …

| **42 FROM TWO NUMBERS** | The suggestions above will give you some ideas. But use your imagination. See how many different ways you can get 42 from two numbers. Be as inventive as you can. |

| **42 FROM SEVERAL NUMBERS** | **'Can you do Addition?' the White Queen asked. 'What's one and one and one and one and one and one and one and one and one and one?'** |

'I don't know,' said Alice. 'I lost count.'

'She can't do Addition,' the Red Queen interrupted.

from *Through the Looking Glass* by Lewis Carroll

The answer to the White Queen's question is not 42, but you *could* make 42 in that way. There are other ways of making 42.

1 (*a*) 'What's 3 and 3 and 3 and ...'
How many 3s do you need to make 42?

(*b*) How else can you make 42 in this kind of way?

2 $3 + 4 + 5 + 6 + 7 + 8 + 9 = 42$

How else can you make 42 from adding *consecutive* numbers?

3 $7 \times 6 = 42$

How else can you make 42 by multiplying numbers together?

4 $420 \div 10 = 42$

How else can you make 42 by dividing numbers?

5 $44 - 43 + 42 - 41 + 40 = 42$

How else can you make 42 from consecutive numbers if you
use − and + signs alternately?

6 $12 + 11 + 10 - 9 + 8 + 7 - 6 + 5 + 4 = 42$

How else can you make 42 from consecutive numbers if you can
use + and − signs in any order?

7 Invent your own rules for how 42 should be made.

See if someone else can make 42 with your rules.

E14
page
84

8 Now choose a different number, instead of 42.

Answer questions 1 to 7 for this new number.

**YOU COULD
USE:**

You could use *Spread*. Choose 3 columns and 6 rows.

1 Put the formula A + B in column C.

Find six ways of putting numbers in columns A and B to produce 42 in
column C.

(Remember to press U to update the table.)

2 Put the formula A * B in column C.

Find six ways of putting numbers in columns A and B to produce 42 in
column C.

3 Try using other formulae in column C.

SHAPING UP TO 42

You need squared paper for questions 1 and 2.

 The **perimeter** of a shape is the distance round the edge of it.

1 The perimeter of this is 42.

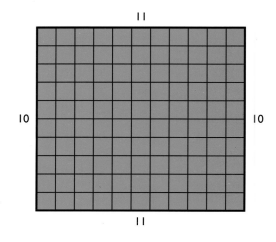

Draw some more rectangles with a perimeter of 42.

2 The area of this shape is 42.

		1	2								
	3	4	5	6							
7	8	9	10	11	12						
13	14	15	16	17	18	19	20				
21	22	23	24	25	26	27	28	29	30		
31	32	33	34	35	36	37	38	39	40	41	42

Draw some more shapes with an area of 42.

3 (a) What is the volume of this cuboid?

You might find interlocking cubes useful for question 3.

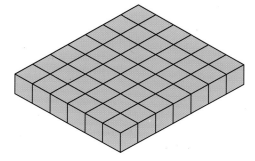

(b) Find some more cuboids with a volume of 42.

(c) Find some cuboids with a surface area of 42.

You need isometric paper for question 4.

4 Draw on isometric paper some shapes which have a perimeter of 42.

Or an area of 42.

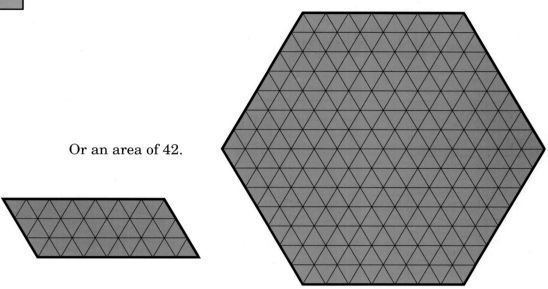

5 Find a square with a perimeter of 42.

6 Find a square with an area of 42.

7 Make up some questions about other shapes which give you an answer of 42. The pictures below show some of the shapes you could use. Or you could use any other shapes you choose.

You might find the resource sheet *'Shapes'* helpful.

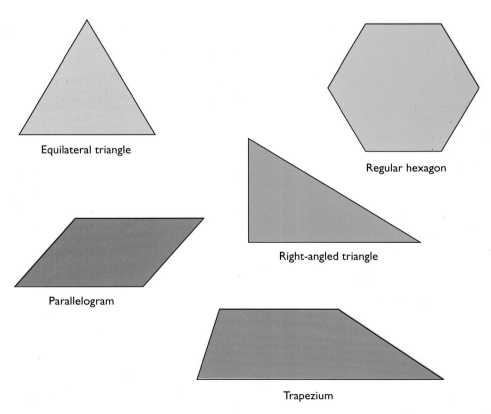

Equilateral triangle

Regular hexagon

Right-angled triangle

Parallelogram

Trapezium

E15
page
84

14 MODELS MADE FROM SQUARES AND TRIANGLES

MAKING POLYHEDRA

For this activity you need some squares and triangles which can be fixed together.

1 Here are two polyhedra made from triangles.

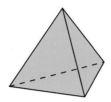

Polyhedron made from 4 triangles.

Polyhedron made from 16 triangles.

Make some polyhedra using just triangles.

For each polyhedron record:

- the number of triangles you use
- the number of vertices
- the number of edges.

Look for patterns in your results.

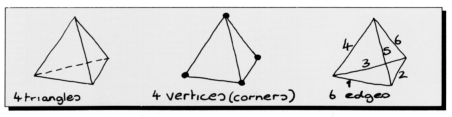

4 triangles   4 vertices (corners)   6 edges

You could use isometric dot paper for question 2.

2 Here are two polyhedra made from squares.

6 squares
6 square faces.

10 squares
2 square faces
4 rectangular faces.

Draw sketches of some more polyhedra made from squares.

For each polyhedron record:

- the number of squares
- the number of square faces
- the number of rectangular faces.

3 Each face of a cube is a square.

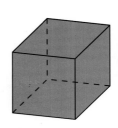

> You might disagree about what you mean by vertices and edges.

(a) Make a *different* polyhedron for which each face is a square. (It should not be a cube.)

(b) How many edges and vertices does this polyhedron have?

(c) Discuss your answers with other people.

4 Here is a polyhedron made from squares *and* triangles.

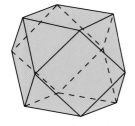

6 squares, 8 triangles

(a) Make some polyhedra from squares *and* triangles.

Record the number of squares and triangles you use for each polyhedron.

(b) Now record the number of squares and triangles other people have used for each of their polyhedra.

(c) Use a graph to show the results.

Put as many points as you can on the graph.

(d) Look for patterns on the graph.

(e) Is it possible for two *different* polyhedra to be represented by the same point on the graph?

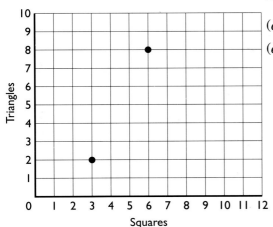

ODD ONE OUT

Choose three polyhedra. Think of a way in which two of them are the same and the other one is different.

Get other people to guess which one is different. Get them to guess why.

> You need several polyhedra for this activity. Use the polyhedra you and other people have made.

75

NAMING THE SHAPES

1 These shapes are all **prisms.**

  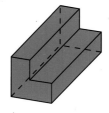

(*a*) Discuss with other people what **prism** means.

(*b*) Which of the shapes you have made are prisms?

2 These shapes are all **pyramids.**

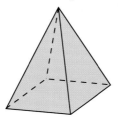 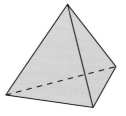 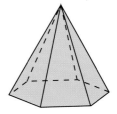

(*a*) Discuss what **pyramid** means.

(*b*) Which of the shapes you have made are pyramids?

3 These shapes are regular **polyhedra.**

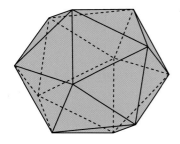

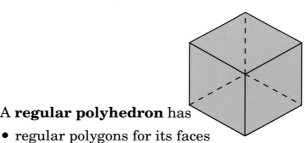

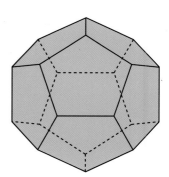

A **regular polyhedron** has

- regular polygons for its faces
- all its faces the same
- all its corners looking the same.

Which of the shapes you have made are regular polyhedra?

NETS

1 This is a **net** of a cube. If you cut this out and fold it up it makes a cube.

Find all the *different* possible nets for a cube.
Here are some things to think about.

- What do you mean by *different*?
- Which of your nets are symmetrical?
- How do you know when you have found all the nets?

You need squared paper for questions 1 and 2.

2 Here is a net of a cube with tabs. The tabs can be used to stick the cube together.

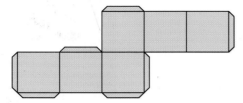

Choose a net of a cube. Show where the tabs could go on your net.

Here are some things to think about.

- In how many different ways could you arrange the tabs on your net?
- Do different nets need different numbers of tabs?

You need isometric paper for questions 3 and 4.

3 Here is a net of a tetrahedron.

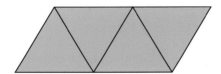

Find all the different nets for a tetrahedron.

Put tabs on one of the nets.

- How many nets?
- How many tabs on each net?
- How many ways of arranging the tabs?

4 Here is the net of a regular octahedron.

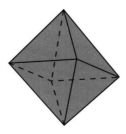 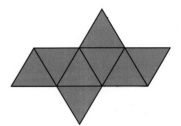

Find all the different nets for an octahedron.

Choose one net. Put tabs on it.

- In how many different ways could you arrange the tabs on your chosen net?
- Do different nets need different numbers of tabs?
- Which nets are symmetrical?
- How many different nets are there?
- How do you know when you have found them all?

15 BINGO

You probably know how to play Bingo.

Every player has a card. Numbers are chosen by chance in some way. If the number chosen is on your card you cover it up.

The first player to cover up all their numbers wins.

BINGO WITH ONE DICE

2		3	
	2		6

Here is a way of playing Bingo.

- Find one or more other people to play with. You could play this game with the whole class.

- Make up your own Bingo card. It should have four numbers.

The numbers can be all different or some of them can be the same.

- Take it in turns to throw a dice.

- If the number on the dice is the same as the number on your card, cover it up or cross it out. Only cross out *one* number at a time.

- The winner is the first person to cross out all their numbers. The game then comes to an end.

1 Play this game two or three times.

2 Now answer the following questions.

   (a) Is it better to choose numbers that are all different or to repeat some numbers?

   (b) Is 6 a sensible number to put on your card?

3 Play the game ten times. Record how long each game is. (How long means how many times you have to throw the dice before somebody wins.)

4 (a) Will the game be shorter or longer if more people play?

   (b) Every time two people play a game will it be the same length?

I In one classroom 8 groups of people played Bingo. There were 3 or 4 people in each group. Each group played ten games. So altogether, 80 games were played.

This bar chart shows how long the games were.

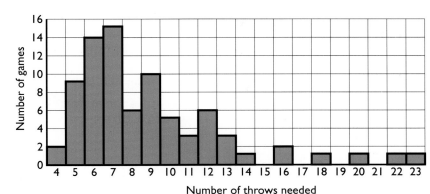

The bar chart shows that in 9 of the games 5 throws were needed, before somebody won.

'If our group of four people play Bingo, how many throws will we need?'

5 (*a*) How many games took 12 throws to win?
(*b*) How many games took 15 throws to win?
(*c*) How many throws did the longest game take?
(*d*) How many throws did the shortest game take?

6 What answer would you give to the girl's question?

7 (*a*) Collect the results for all the games played in your class.
(*b*) Draw a bar chart to show the results.
(*c*) How many throws did the longest game take?
(*d*) How many throws did the shortest game take?

YOU COULD USE:

This is how the computer program *Spread* could be used instead of a dice.

* Set up *Spread* with 1 row and 1 column.
* Enter this formula

    A = RND (6)

Every time you press U, the computer will 'throw a dice' again.

This is how you can get *Spread* to count the number of throws.

* Have 2 columns.
* Change the name of the second column to COUNT.
* Enter this formula in the second column.

    COUNT = COUNT + 1

* Now enter 0 in the second column.

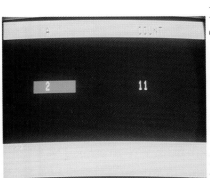

Every time you press U, the computer will throw a dice and will add 1 to the count.

USING MORE NUMBERS

1 (a) Play the game ten times using eight numbers instead of four.

Think carefully about which numbers to choose.

(b) Write down how long each game is.

(c) Compare your results for eight numbers with your results for four numbers. Do your results surprise you?

I A class wanted to compare the results for eight numbers with the results for four numbers.

Here is the bar chart they drew.

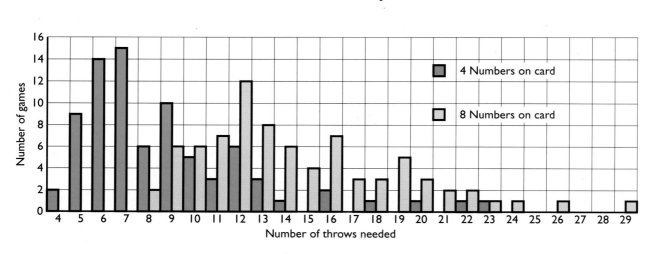

One way they thought of to compare the lengths of the games was to look at the **mode.**

The **mode** is the commonest number of throws.

For this class, when four numbers were used, the mode was 7 throws (7 throws happened 15 times).

---

2 What was the mode for this class, when eight numbers were used?

3 (a) Collect the results for all the games played in your class with eight numbers.

(b) Draw a bar chart in two colours to show the class results for both types of game.

(c) What is the mode for your class when four numbers are used?

(d) What is the mode for your class when eight numbers are used?

'We are going to play some games of Bingo with twelve numbers.'

4 How long would you expect each of these games to last?

A different way of comparing the game with four numbers with the game with eight numbers is to use the **mean** instead of the **mode.**

To find the **mean** number of throws for each game, you first need to find the total number of throws. You then divide by the number of games.

Look at the bar chart on the opposite page.

This is how to find the mean number of throws for games with four numbers.

The total number of throws is

$2 \times 4 + 9 \times 5 + 14 \times 6 + 15 \times 7 + 6 \times 8 + 10 \times 9 + 5 \times 10 + 3 \times 11 + 6 \times 12 + 3 \times 13 + 1 \times 14 + 2 \times 16 + 1 \times 18 + 1 \times 20 + 1 \times 22 + 1 \times 23 = 703$

The mean number of throws is $703 \div 80 = 8.8$

5 Look at the bar chart on the oppposite page.

Find the mean number of throws for games with eight numbers.

6 Look at your class results.

(*a*) Find the mean number of throws for games with four numbers.

(*b*) Find the mean number of throws for games with eight numbers.

7 What do you think would be the mean number of throws for games with twelve numbers?

BINGO WITH TWO DICE

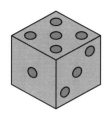

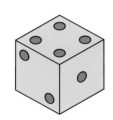

Now play a different game of Bingo.

- Use two dice instead of one.

- Each time the dice are thrown, *add the two numbers they show*. This is the number you cross off.

- Write eight numbers on your Bingo card. Think carefully about which numbers to use. They can be all different or some of them can be the same.

1 Play this version of the game ten times.

   Record how long each game is. Keep the numbers you wrote down for each game.

2 Answer the following questions.

   (*a*) Did you change your strategy after playing one or two games?

   (*b*) Were the later games shorter or longer than the earlier games? Can you explain why?

   (*c*) Were the games with two dice shorter or longer than the games with one dice? Can you explain why?

E17
page
85

YOU COULD STILL USE:

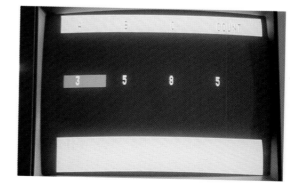

This is how *Spread* could be used instead of two dice.

- Set up *Spread* with 1 row and 4 columns.

- Change the name of the fourth column to COUNT.

- Enter these formula

      A = RND (6)
      B = RND (6)
      C = A + B
      COUNT = COUNT + 1

- Now enter 0 in the fourth column.

Every time you press U the computer will throw two dice, it will add their numbers together, and it will add 1 to the count.

WHAT HAPPENS IF?

You could use *Spread* by changing column C to C = ABS (A – B)

What happens if you change the rule for getting the number from the two dice?

1 Play Bingo with two dice again.

- This time, instead of adding the numbers shown on the dice, *take the smaller number away from the bigger number.*

6	5	5	4
4	3	2	1

- Think carefully about what eight numbers to put on your Bingo card.

Play the game several times, so that you get better at choosing which numbers to put on your card.

You could use *Spread* by changing column C to C = A * B.

2 Now change the rule again.

- This time, *multiply the two numbers shown on the dice.*

36	35	34	33
32	31	30	29

- Think carefully about what eight numbers to put on your card this time.

Play the game several times.

3 Use three dice. Decide whether to add, subtract or multiply the numbers. Investigate what happens.

H25
page
137

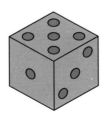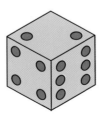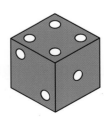

REVIEW EXERCISES E

EXERCISE 14 Number 3

> Do not use a calculator until you have to.

1 The answer is 100

(a) 50 + ...   (b) 30 + ...   (c) 98 + ...

(d) 4 + ...   (e) 71 + ...   (f) 37 + ...

2 The answer is 1000

(a) 600 +   (b) 50 + ...   (c) 560 + ...

(d) 987 + ...   (e) 387 + ...   (f) 234 + ...

3 The answer is 10

(a) 23 – ...   (b) 56 – ...

(c) ... – 67   (d) ... – 452

4 The answer is 280

(a) 480 – ...   (b) 360 – ...   (c) 538 – ...

(d) ... – 340   (e) ... – 832   (f) ... –489

5 The answer is 12

(a) 6 × ...   (b) 3 × ...   (c) 12 × ...

(d) 24 ÷ ...   (e) 120 ÷ ...   (f) 240 ÷ ...

6 The answer is 60

(a) 6 × ...   (b) 20 × ...   (c) 5 × ...

(d) 60 ÷ ...   (e) 180 ÷ ...   (f) 1200 ÷ ...

EXERCISE 15 Area and perimeter

1 (a) Copy these letters onto centimetre-squared paper.

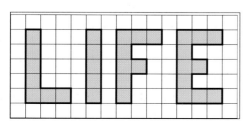

(b) The perimeter of letter L is 16 cm.
Find the perimeter of the other letters.

(c) The area of letter L is 7 cm².
Find the area of the other letters.

2 Copy these shapes onto centimetre-squared paper. Find the area of each shape.

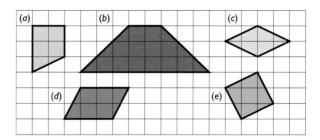

3 (a) The perimeter of an equilateral triangle is 18 cm. Find the length of one of the sides.

(b) The perimeter of a rhombus is 20 cm. Find the length of one of the sides.

(c) The perimeter of an isosceles triangle is 20 cm. The length of one side is 8 cm. Find the lengths of the other sides. (There are two answers.)

4 Find the area of these shapes.

(a)

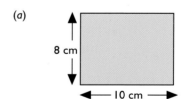

(b)

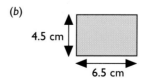

(c)

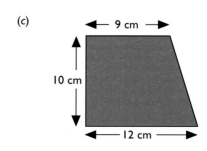

EXERCISE 16 Solid shapes 2

1
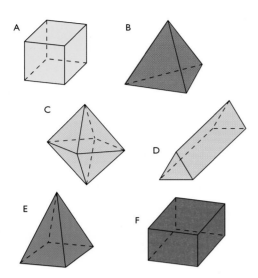

(a) Which of the shapes are pyramids?

(b) Which of the shapes are prisms?

(c) Which of the shapes are regular polyhedra?

2 Look at the shapes in question 1.

(a) How many vertices does each shape have? (A vertex is a corner.)

(b) How many edges does each shape have?

(c) How many faces does each shape have?

(d) Here is a rule about the number of vertices, edges and faces of a solid shape. It is called Euler's rule.

VERTICES + FACES = EDGES + 2

Use Euler's rule to check your answers for (a), (b) and (c).

3 This is the net of a solid.

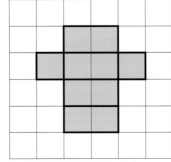

(a) What is the solid called?

(b) Draw a different net for the same solid.

4 Here is a cuboid.

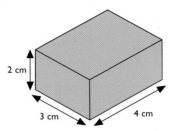

Draw a net for this cuboid.
Put tabs on your net so that the net could be glued together.

EXERCISE 17 Handling data 2

1 40 women were asked how many children they had. Here are the results.

Number of children	Number of women
0	10
1	14
2	7
3	4
4	2
5	2
6	0
7	1

(a) What is the mode for the number of children?

(b) What is the median number of children?

(c) Calculate the mean number of children.

2 A red dice and a blue dice are thrown. One possible outcome is 4 on the red dice and 5 on the blue dice. List all the possible outcomes.
(Think of a way of doing this without too much writing.)

3 When a dart is thrown at a dart board there are many different outcomes. The dart can go in any number from 1 to 20. In each number it can go in single, or double, or treble. Instead of going in a number the dart can go in the 25, the 50 (or bull) or miss altogether.

How many outcomes are there for a dart?

16 NUMBER CHAINS

I This flow chart shows how to create a chain of numbers.

Input
number

No ← Is it even ? → Yes

Subtract
1

Halve
it

If you start with the number 11 this is how the chain starts:

$11 \rightarrow 10 \rightarrow 5 \rightarrow 4\ldots$

1 What happens eventually to the chain that starts with 11?

2 Create other number chains by starting with different numbers. What happens to the chains eventually?

3 The number 6 could be called a 4-stage number, because it takes 4 stages to reach zero.

What would you call these numbers:

5?   8?   11?   12?

4 Is there more than one 5-stage number?

5 (a) What is the biggest 7-stage number?

(b) What is the smallest 7-stage number?

6 (a) Which number less than 20 takes most stages to reach zero?

(b) Which number less than 100 takes most stages to reach zero?

YOU COULD USE:

Here is a *Basic* program you could use.

```
10 INPUT N
20 IF (N MOD 2) = 0 THEN N = N/2 ELSE N = N−1
30 PRINT N
40 IF N > 0 THEN 20
```

Here is a *Logo* procedure you could use.

```
SEQ :N
PRINT :N
IF :N = 0 [STOP]
IF (REMAINDER :N 2) = 0 [SEQ :N/2] [SEQ :N-1]
END
```

If you want to use
Spread instead,
see page 89.

You could use computer programs for any of the activities. If you change the rule you need to change line 20 of the *Basic* program or the long line of the *Logo* procedure.

You might also want to change line 40 of the *Basic* program, or the STOP line of the *Logo* procedure.

WHAT HAPPENS IF?

I What happens if you change the rules for creating chains? You get different number chains by using this flow chart.

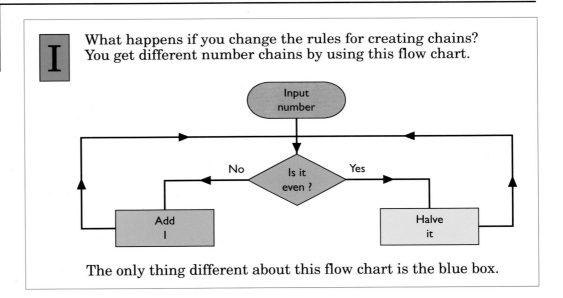

The only thing different about this flow chart is the blue box.

1 If you start with the number 11, what chain do you get? What happens to the chain eventually?

2 Try starting with other numbers. What happens to each chain eventually?

3 11 is a ☐-stage number

   Decide what number should go in the box above. You might want to discuss your decision with someone else.

4 What is the biggest 7-stage number?

5 (*a*) Which number less than 20 has the most stages?

   (*b*) Which number less than 100 has the most stages?

MORE BLUE CHANGES

Now use a different blue box. Here are some possibilities.

> Add
> 3

> Add
> 5

> Add
> 4

For each rule say what happens eventually.

Discuss what could be meant by a 7-stage number for each rule.

Investigate which numbers take the most stages.

A PINK CHANGE

Instead of the pink box in the flow chart you could use this:

> Is it a
> multiple
> of 3 ?

You could then use blue and yellow boxes.

> Add
> 1

> Divide by
> 3

1 What happens eventually when this rule is used?

Investigate stages for this rule.

2 Now try different blue boxes. Here are some possibilities.

> Add
> 2

> Subtract
> 4

> Add
> 6

3 What happens if you use this blue box?

> Multiply by 2
> and then add 1

This is what someone who used this rule said:

'There seems to be two types of starting numbers.'

What do you think she meant? Why does it happen like that?

A DRASTIC CHANGE

You could use the following boxes as the pink, blue and yellow boxes.

Is it even ?

| Square the number and then subtract 1 | | Halve the number |

1 What happens eventually when this rule is used?

'I think 13 is really unlucky.'

F18
page
98

Do you think he has a point?
What other numbers are unlucky?

2 Make up your own drastic changes and investigate them.

USING SPREAD

This is how you get *Spread* to produce the sequence on page 86.

- Set up *Spread* with 1 row and 4 columns.
- Enter these formulae:

      A = D
      B = A MOD 2
      C = 1–B
      D = (A–1) * B + (A/2) * C

- Enter the starting number in D
- Keep pressing U.

You can get most of the other sequences by changing the formula in D.

To get the sequences in *'A pink change'* you need to change the formula in B as well.

POLYGON ARRANGEMENTS

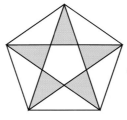
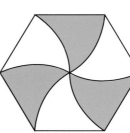
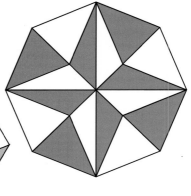

> If you cannot use MATs, cut shapes from the resource sheet *'Regular polygons'*.

For some of the activities in this task you need some polygons to arrange or to colour. You could cut your own polygons from paper or card. It is easier to use polygons which are already made. We recommend ATM MATs. The MATs have patterns on one side and are plain on the other.

SYMMETRICAL ARRANGEMENTS OF SQUARES

I Some 2-dimensional patterns are symmetrical. There are two types of symmetry. The first is called **mirror symmetry.**

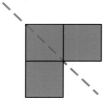

Figure 1

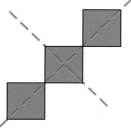

Figure 2

Figure 1 shows a pattern made from three squares. It has mirror symmetry. The dotted line is the **mirror line.**

Figure 2 shows a different pattern made from three squares. This pattern has two **mirror lines.**

The second type of symmetry is called **rotational symmetry.**

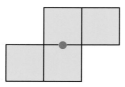

Figure 3

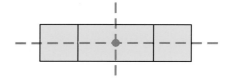

Figure 4

Figure 3 shows a pattern made from 4 squares. It has rotational symmetry. The red dot is the centre of rotation. Make the pattern by arranging four squares on a sheet of paper. Now turn the paper through half a turn around the red dot. The pattern still looks the same.

Figure 4 has both types of symmetry.

Use the plain side
of the ATM MATs
for the questions
on this page.

1 Make some symmetrical arrangements of three squares.

2 Make some symmetrical arrangements of four squares.

3 Make some arrangements of three squares which are not symmetrical.
   And four squares.

4 Make an arrangement of five squares with mirror symmetry. Make an
   arrangement of five squares with rotational symmetry.

5 Compare the patterns you have made with the patterns other people
   have made. How many people have had the same ideas? How many
   different ideas are there?

ARRANGING OTHER POLYGONS

1 Make some symmetrical arrangements using three triangles.

2 Make some symmetrical arrangements using seven hexagons.

3 Choose a type of polygon. Choose how many polygons of this type you
   want to use. Make symmetrical arrangements.

4 Make a symmetrical arrangement. Now take one of the polygons away
   so that the arrangement is not symmetrical any more. Get someone
   else to try to put the polygon back to make the symmetrical
   arrangement.

   Did they put the polygon back where you expected?

5 Make a symmetrical arrangement using polygons of more than one
   type.

F19
page
99

SQUARES WITHIN SQUARES

Draw a big square using
sixteen squares, as shown.

Draw a tilted square on the big square. The inside of this tilted square
is coloured red. The rest is coloured blue.

For this activity
you can use
squared paper.

How many little squares are all red?
How many little squares are all blue?
How many are half red and half blue?

Try the same thing for a big square made from four squares. From 36
squares. From 64 squares. ... Can you find any rules for the numbers
of squares of each type?

WHAT HAPPENS IF?

1 What happens if you draw *rectangles* inside the big squares? The rectangles can be nearly squares …

  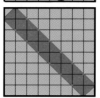

or they can be as narrow as possible …

Or...

2 What happens if you make a big square from an odd number of squares? You could use 9 squares. You could draw a rectangle inside …

or you could draw a square.

D13
page
68

What if the big square is made from 25 squares? Or 49 squares? Or …

WHAT HAPPENS IF INSTEAD?

1 What happens if you use triangles instead of squares?

2 What happens if you make a hexagon from the triangles?

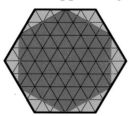

3 What happens if the triangle or the hexagon has sides of odd length?

 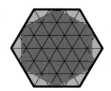

HALF AND HALF

The ATM MATs have designs printed on them.

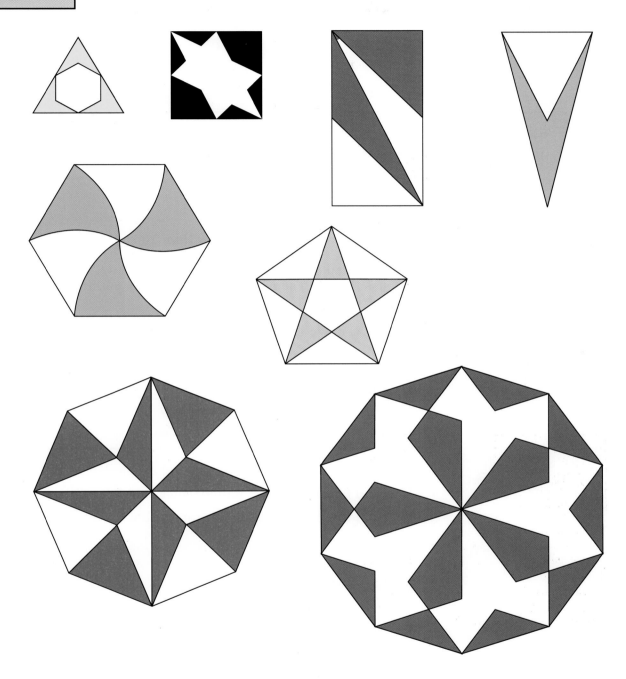

1 For all these ATM MATs, except one, half of the area is coloured and half is white. Which ATM MAT is different?

2 Make up your own polygon designs, so that half of each polygon is coloured.

3 You might want to make up polygon designs using four colours. Each colour could cover a quarter of the area.

18 PALINDROMES

Pip   33   Radar

Toot   73637   Madam

2442   Reviver   474

FINDING PALINDROMES

 Palindromes are words or numbers which are the same if the letters or digits are reversed.

1   Write down all the numbers less than 100 which are palindromes.

You will need to decide whether numbers like 5 are palindromes. Discuss this with someone else. How many palindromes less than 100 are there?

2   (*a*)   Write down six three-digit palindromes.

     (*b*)   How many palindromes less than 1000 are there?

3   (*a*)   Write down six four-digit palindromes.

     (*b*)   How many palindromes less than 10 000 are there?

PALINDROME MULTIPLES

You will find an explanation of what *multiples* are on page 10.

1   (*a*)   Which palindromes less than 100 are multiples of 11?

     (*b*)   Find four three-digit palindromes that are multiples of 11.

     (*c*)   Find some four-digit palindromes that are multiples of 11.

2   (*a*)   Write down all the two-digit palindromes which are multiples of 9.

     (*b*)   Write down all the three-digit palindromes which are multiples of 9.

     (*c*)   Find some four-digit palindromes which are multiples of 9.

3   Investigate palindromes that are multiples of other numbers.

4   Divide several four-digit palindromes by 11. What do you notice? Discuss your answers with someone else.

REVERSE AND ADD

 The number 23 is not a palindrome. If you reverse 23 you get 32.

23 + 32 = 55

55 is a palindrome.

Here is what happens with the number 68.

68 + 86 = 154
154 + 451 = 605
605 + 506 = 1111

1111 is a palindrome. So:

23 takes 1 step to become a palindrome;
68 takes 3 steps to become a palindrome.

1 How many steps does it take for 48 to become a palindrome?
Try some other numbers.

2 Which number less than 50 takes most steps to become a palindrome?

3 Some numbers take a lot of steps. One of these is 89. How many steps does 89 take to become a palindrome?

4 Some numbers never seem to become palindromes. Nobody knows whether the number 196 ever becomes a palindrome. Perhaps you could try to find out.

REVERSE AND SUBTRACT

 The number 62 is not a palindrome. If you reverse 62 you get 26.

62 – 26 = 36
63 – 36 = 27
72 – 27 = 45
54 – 45 = 9

Earlier you were asked to decide whether you would call numbers like 9 palindromes. Here it is assumed that 9 is a palindrome.

So, when you subtract, 62 takes 4 steps to become a palindrome.

1 Investigate what happens with other two-digit numbers.

2 Investigate what happens with some three-digit numbers.

3 What happens to the number 9625? Try some other four-digit numbers.

PALINDROMIC TIMES, DATES AND MONEY

  Here are two times written using the 24-hour clock.

Both of these times are palindromes.

1 Find all the palindromic times, using the 24-hour clock.

  29th March 1992 is palindromic date if it is written like this:

29 – 3 – 92.

2 (*a*) What other dates in 1992 are palindromic?
   (*b*) What is the last palindromic date in the 1980s?
   (*c*) What is the last palindromic date this century?
   (*d*) What is the first palindromic date in your lifetime?

  £35.53 is a palindromic amount of money.

3 A game costs between £20 and £30. The amount it costs is palindromic.

   (*a*) How much could it have cost?
       (There are several possible answers.)

   (*b*) Sharon buys the game with three £10 notes.
       The change she gets is five different coins.

   How much did the game cost?

SQUARE NUMBERS

Find some square numbers which are palindromes.

> You will find an explanation of what **square numbers** are on page 106.

PALINDROMIC FACTORS

  4 is a **factor** of 12, because 12 divides exactly by 4.

The factors of 12 are 1, 2, 3, 4, 6 and 12.

1 The year 1991 was a palindromic year. What is the next palindromic year after 1991?
2 All the factors of 1991 are palindromes! Find some other palindromes like 1991.

WHAT STAYS THE SAME WHEN YOU REVERSE?

 A palindrome is a number which stays the same when you reverse it.

Numbers which are not palidromes do not stay the same. But some things about the numbers might stay the same.

For example, the number 438 is a multiple of 3. The number 834 is also a multiple of 3.

1 Do all multiples of 3 stay multiples of 3 when you reverse them?

2 Find an even number which stays even when you reverse it. Do all even numbers stay even numbers when you reverse them?

3 Do all three-digit numbers stay three-digit numbers when you reverse them?

4 (*a*) Find a multiple of 5 which stays a multiple of 5, when you reverse it. Do all multiples of 5 stay multiples of 5, when you reverse them?

   (*b*) What about multiple of 9? Multiples of 11? Other multiples?

 A **prime number** is a number with exactly two factors.

7 is a prime number. Its factors are 1 and 7.

6 is **not** a prime number. Its factors are 1, 2, 3 and 6.

5 Find a prime number which stays a prime number when you reverse it.

6 Find a square number which stays a square number when you reverse it.

 A **triangular number** is a number which can be arranged in the shape of a triangle.

1, 3, 6 and 10 are the first four triangular numbers.

7 Find a triangle number which stays a triangle number when you reverse it.

8 Investigate whether other properties of numbers stay the same when

REVIEW EXERCISES F

Number machines

1 Here is a number machine

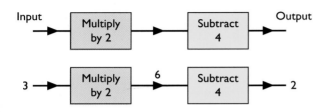

(a) You put in 5. What number do you get?

(b) You put in 10. What number do you get?

(c) You put in a number and get the same number out. What number did you put in?

(d) You put in a number and get 10 out. what number did you put in?

2

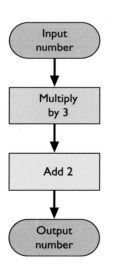

(a) The input is 2. What is the output?

(b) The input is 4. What is the output?

(c) The input is 13. What is the output?

(d) The input is 329. What is the output?

(e) The output is 11. What was the input?

(f) The output is 23. What was the input?

(g) The output is 833. What was the input?

3

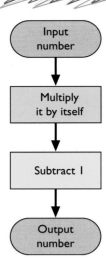

(a) The input is 3. What is the output?

(b) The input is 6. What is the output?

(c) The input is 276. What is the output?

(d) The output is 15. What was the input?

(e) The output is 99. What was the input?

(f) The output is 9800. What was the input?

(g) The input is even. What can you say about the output?

(h) The output ends in 4. What can you say about the input?

4

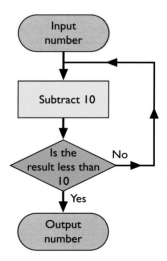

(a) The input is 18. What is the output?

(b) The input is 32. What is the output?

(c) The input is 20. What is the output?

(d) The output is 6. Write down three possible inputs.

(e) The input is 4327. What is the output?

5

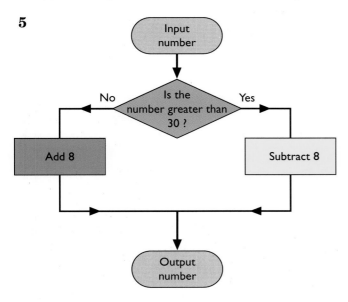

(a) The input is 25. What is the output?

(b) The input is 35. What is the output?

(c) Which numbers can be output from two different inputs?

■ 6 A number machine produces these results.

Input	Output
6	3
10	5
3	9
7	21
11	33
8	4

Draw a flowchart for this machine.

EXERCISE 19 Symmetry

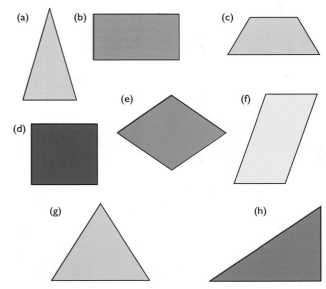

1 Some of these shapes have line symmetry. Copy the shapes which have line symmetry. Draw in the lines of symmetry. (Some shapes have more than one line of symmetry.)

2 Which of the shapes in question 1 have rotational symmetry?

3 Copy each of these shapes onto squared paper.

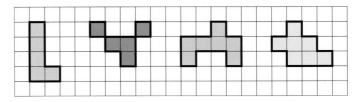

Shade one extra square on each shape so that the shape has line symmetry.

4 Copy each of these shapes onto squared paper.

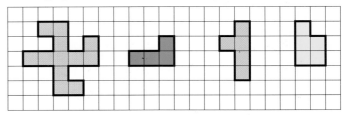

Shade one extra square on each shape so that the shape has rotational symmetry but no line of symmetry.

19 FOOD

Most people like eating food.

Some people like cooking food. Some people like talking about it. Some people even like buying it.

| **FAVOURITE FOOD** |

1 (*a*) What are your favourite foods? Write down all your favourite foods you can think of.

(*b*) Pick one food which is your absolute favourite.

2 Find out the favourite foods for your class.

- You can do this by collecting some information.
- You can talk about how to do this with other members of your class.

Things to decide

- Are you collecting information about *any* favourite food?

  You could stick to snacks only.
  Or main courses only.
  Or puddings only.
  Or only breakfast food.
  Or …

- Are you collecting:

  one absolute favourite from each person.
  or several favourites.

POPULAR FOOD

What is your name? _____

What gender are you? ☐ female
                      ☐ male

What is your favourite food?
☐ baked beans   ☐ sausages
☐ burgers   ☐ crisps
☐ ice cream   ☐ fish fingers
☐ chips   ☐ fresh fruit
☐ chocolate   ☐ doughnuts
☐ cheese   ☐ something
☐ cake   else

You could use a computer to design a data collection sheet.

The questions you ask on the data collection sheet for *your* class will depend on the decisions you have made.

When you have collected the information, you could put it into a computer.

3 You could now answer questions like these about favourite foods.

- What is the most popular favourite food in the class?
- How many people said it was their favourite?
- What percentage of the class said it was their favourite?
- What is the most popular main course?

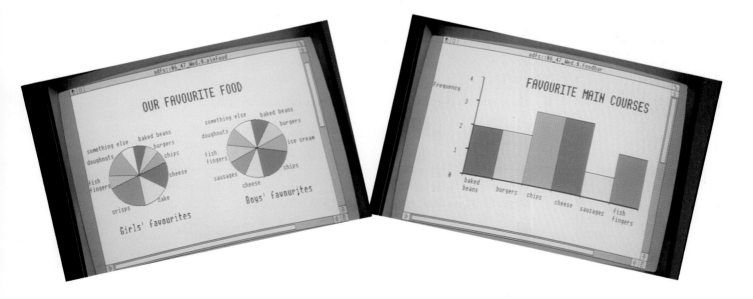

Produce a report or a poster about what you have found. You could use some graphs to help explain your results.

E17
page
85

4 You might want to ask different people about their favourite foods. Ask older people. Do they have different ideas from the ideas in your class?

GUESS THE WEIGHT

You will find it easier to understand this activity if you collect the information for yourself. If this really is a problem you could use the resource sheet 'Cupfuls'.

To help you answer question 3 you could find out how many millilitres your cup holds.

For this activity you need some scales.

Here is a list of foods.

Sultanas	Beans
Sugar	Flour
Salt	Cornflakes
Rice	Milk
Lentils	Pasta shapes

You can add your own ideas to the list.

1 Find the weight of a cupful of each food on your list.

2 Rewrite your list in order of weight, starting with the lightest.

3 Now find how much a litre jugful of each food on the list weighs.

4 How much does a pint jugful of each food weigh?

5 How much does a teaspoonful of each food weigh?

6 How much does a bucketful of each food weigh?

7 How much does a bathful of each food weigh?

G20
page
116

PREPARING A MEAL

When you have a meal, you often eat several different things. You might eat sausages *and* potatoes *and* beans.

This means cooking the sausages *and* potatoes *and* beans, so that they are all ready at the same time.

So, to prepare this meal you need to answer these questions.

• How long do sausages take to cook?
• How long do potatoes take to cook?
• How long do beans take to cook?
• What do you have to do *before* cooking sausages?
• What do you have to do *before* cooking potatoes?
• What do you have to do *before* cooking beans?

1 Find out the answers to the questions on page 102.

Now decide what you need to do *first* to get this meal ready.

I Look at this drawing. It is called a **network diagram**.
It shows what you need to do to make a cup of tea.

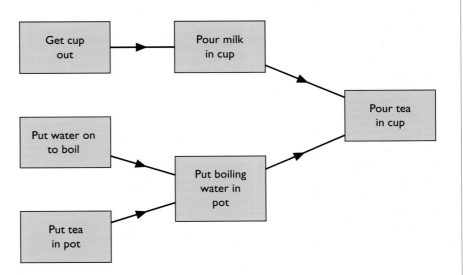

Each of the things to do is written in a box. The way the boxes
are joined together shows the order in which the things need to
be done.

Discuss the drawing with other people in your class.

2 Draw a network diagram for preparing a meal of sausages, potatoes
and beans.

Here are some of the statements you need to put onto your diagram.
Think what other statements you need before drawing your diagram.

> Peel and cut up the potatoes.
> Put the potatoes into a pan of water.
> Cook the beans.
> Dish up the sausages.
> Eat the meal.
> Find some plates.
> Grill the sausages.
> Take the sausages out of the packet.
> Weigh the potatoes.

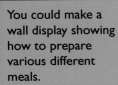

You could make a
wall display showing
how to prepare
various different
meals.

3 Think of a different meal you might want to prepare. Or ask someone
else how they prepare a meal.

Draw a network diagram to explain how this meal is prepared.

RECITES

If you cannot collect your own recipes use the resource sheet 'Recipes'.

You might want to choose a different number instead of 6. If there are 5 people in your family you could rewrite the recipes, so that they are suitable for 5 people.

1 (*a*) Collect some recipes.

Each person in the class could bring in a recipe. Perhaps you could bring in the recipe for your favourite dish.

(*b*) Look at the recipes you have collected.

Does the recipe say how many people it is for? If it doesn't you will have to guess. You can discuss this with other people in the class.

(*c*) Rewrite each of the recipes, so that it is suitable for 6 people. This means you will have to change the quantities given in the recipes.

Pease Porridge (1695)

Serves 6–8

2 lb shin of beef (beef shank)
1 large onion
4 stalks (sticks) celery
2 carrots
1 tbs salt
10 peppercorns
1 bay leaf
2 pt broad beans or lima beans
$\frac{1}{4}$ lb bacon
1 lb sorrel, chopped
4 tbs each spearmint and parsley, chopped
1 oz butter
6–8 slices french bread, toasted

Honey and Saffron Quiche

(served to Henry IV at his Coronation Feast in 1399)

Serves 8

$\frac{3}{4}$ pt thick cream
$\frac{1}{8}$ tsp saffron
$\frac{1}{4}$ pt milk
3 eggs plus 2 extra yolks
$\frac{1}{4}$ pt honey
a 9-inch pastry shell, baked blind

To dress dandelions like spinach (1845)

Serves 6

$2\frac{1}{2}$ lbs dandelion shoots
4 lbs butter
$\frac{1}{2}$ tsp salt
$\frac{1}{2}$ tsp pepper

An English Potage (1669)

Serves 8–10

4 oz boneless beef
4 oz boneless mutton or lamb
4 oz boneless veal
$1\frac{1}{2}$ lb chicken pieces (legs, backs, feet, etc.)
4 oz gammon
2 onions, quartered
1 clove garlic
10 peppercorns
5 cloves
3–4 pt water
lettuce, sorrel, borage and bugloss (all boiled for 5 minutes in a little stock)

2 The quantities given in these traditional English recipes are usually in pounds and pints. Change them so that they are in grams (or kilograms) and litres (or millilitres).

 1 pint (pt) is about 0.57 litres.
1 pint (pt) is about 570 millilitres.
1 pound (lb) is about 0.45 kilograms.
1 pound (lb) is about 450 grams.
1 ounce (oz) is about 30 grams.

3 The quantities given in some of the traditional English recipes are quite large.

You might want to choose a different number instead of 4.

Scale the recipes down so that they are suitable for 4 people.

 G21
page
116

20 NUMBER SHAPES

ODD NUMBERS

 These numbers are all **odd** numbers.

3   7   13   341   555   1729

Write down some odd numbers.

Explain to someone else what an odd number is.

EVEN NUMBERS

 These numbers are all **even** numbers.

42   1000   16   98   654

Write down some even numbers.

Explain to someone else what an even number is.

SQUARE NUMBERS

 Here are some **square** numbers.

16   25   81

Find all the square numbers less than 100.

Is 1 a square number? Discuss this with other people.

TRIANGLE NUMBERS

 Here are some **triangle** numbers.

10   36   78

Find all the triangle numbers less than 100.

Is 1 a triangle number? Discuss this with other people.

CUBE NUMBERS

You might find interlocking cubes useful for this activity.

 Here is a **cube** number.

Find all the cube numbers less than 1000.
Is 1 a cube number? Discuss this with other people.

FACTORS AND PRIME NUMBERS

 The **factors** of 6 are 1, 2, 3 and 6.

1 Copy and complete this table:

Number	Factors	Number of factors
1	1	1
2	1,2	
3		
4		
5		
6	1,2,3,6	4
7		
8		
9		
10		
11		
12		

 A **prime** number is a number with exactly *two* factors.

5 is a prime number, because it has exactly two factors: 5 and 1.

2 (*a*) Which numbers less than 20 are prime numbers?
(*b*) Find a prime number bigger than 50.
(*c*) Find a big prime number. How can you be sure that it is prime?

 1 and 4 have an *odd* number of factors
(1 has 1 factor and 4 has 3 factors).

3 (*a*) Which numbers less than 20 have an odd number of factors?
(*b*) Find a number bigger than 50 with an odd number of factors.
(*c*) Find a big number with an odd number of factors.

WHICH NUMBERS LESS THAN 30...?

In the following:

■ means a square number.

P means a prime number.

⬡ means a cube number.

The number 3 is P.

The number 64 is ■ and ⬡ .

The number 13 is ■ + ■ (13 = 9 + 4).

Which numbers less than 30 are:

1 ■ ?

2 ⬡ ?

3 ■ + ■ ?

4 P + P ?

For some of these you might be able to say which numbers less than 100 are …

CONNECTIONS BETWEEN NUMBERS

In the following:

E means an even number.

O means an odd number.

P means a prime number.

■ means a square number.

△ means a triangle number.

⬡ means a cube number.

Some of the following equations are possible and some are not.

For example, there are lots of ways of getting

E + O = O

Here is one way:

14 + 9 = 23

There are no ways of getting O + O = O.

Investigate each of the other equations.

- Are there lots of ways of getting them?
- Are there no ways of getting them?
- Is there only one way of getting any of them?

1 E + O = O

2 E + E = E

3 O + O = E

4 O + O = O

5 O × O = E

6 O × O = O

7 E × E = E

8 E × E = O

9 E × O = E

10 E × O = O

11 ■ + ■ = ■

12 ■ + ■ + ■ = ■

13 △ + △ = ■

14 P + P = ■

15 P + 1 = ■

16 △ + △ = △

17 ■ + ■ = ⬡

EXPLANATIONS

 It is possible to draw pictures to explain some of the equations in *'Connections between numbers'*.

Here is an example.

E + O = O

1 Which equation does each of these pictures explain?

(a)    (b)    (c)

2 What connections between numbers do each of these pictures show?

(a)   (b)   (c)

WHAT IS THE SMALLEST NUMBER?

Some of these numbers are hard to find.

What is the smallest number which is

1 E and △ and ▨ ?

2 ▨ + ▨ in two different ways?

3 ▨ + ▨ + ▨ in two different ways?

4 ▨ + ▨ + ▨ + ▨ in two different ways?

5 ⬡ + ⬡ in two different ways?

6 ⬡ and △ ?

What are the three smallest numbers which are

7 Not P + P?

8 △ and ▨ ?

OPTICAL ILLUSIONS

> You may be confident about your answers to questions 1 and 2. But sometimes our eyes can deceive us!

WHAT DO YOU SEE?

For questions 1 and 2 just use your eyes. Do not use a ruler.

1 Which of these red lines are longer?

2 Which of these blue lines are parallel?

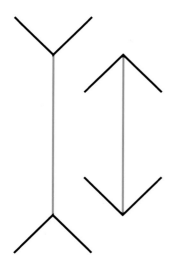

> **Important:** Do *not* change your answer to question 1. What you wrote down is not *wrong*. It is what you *saw*!

3 Measure the lengths of the red lines in question 1. Which line is longer?

LENGTHS OF LINES

Here are six red lines.

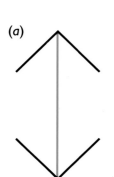
(a)

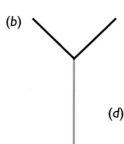
(b)

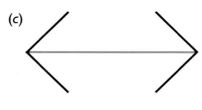
(c)

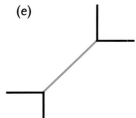
(e)

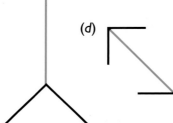
(d)

(f)

1 Do not use a ruler. Make a list of the lines in order of size. Start with the smallest.

2 Discuss your answer to question 1 with other people in your class. Did everyone give the same answer? What differences were there?

3 Now use a ruler. Make a list of the lines in order of size. Start with the smallest.

SQUARES INSIDE SQUARES

Look at these pictures.

(a)
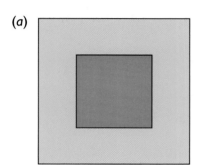

(b)

(c)
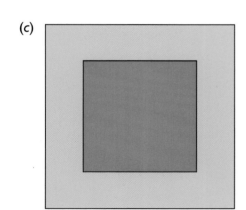

(d)
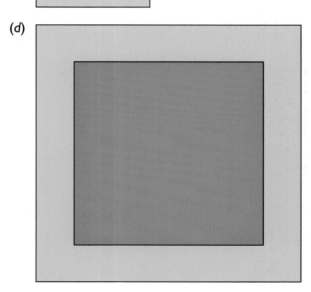

1 Do not use a ruler.

In which pictures is the blue area bigger than the red area?
In which pictures is the red area bigger?
In which pictures are they the same size?

2 Now use a ruler to measure the pictures. Work out the red area and blue area of each picture.

Check your answers to question 1. Did other people see things as you did?

PARALLEL LINES

 Here are some ways of describing **parallel lines.**

- They are always the same distance apart.
- They never meet, even if you continue them for ever.

1 Look at these pairs of lines. Do not use a ruler.

Are the two blue lines parallel?
Are the two red lines parallel?
Are the two yellow lines parallel?
Are the two green lines parallel?
Are the two orange lines parallel?

2 Now use a ruler to check your answers to question 1. (You might still find it hard to tell in some cases.)

I Here is another way of finding out whether lines are **parallel.** Look at the two grey lines. They are parallel. A line has been drawn across the grey lines. The angles marked in red are equal. *These angles are only equal if the lines are parallel.*

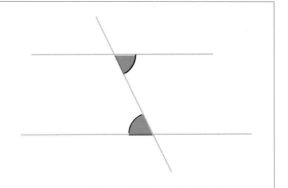

Get the resource
sheet *'Parallel lines'*.

3 Look at question 3 on the resource sheet. The pairs of lines are the same as the lines in question 1.

Look at the pair of blue lines.
Draw a line across it.

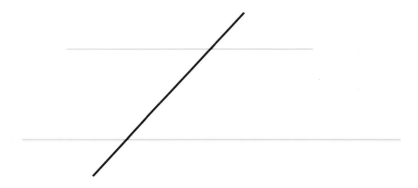

(*a*) Measure the angles. Are the blue lines parallel?

(*b*) Now do the same for all the other pairs of lines. Which pairs of lines are parallel?

(*c*) Are your answers the same as your answers for question 2?

4 Look at question 4 on the resource sheet.

Two of the lines are parallel.

Measure all the angles. Colour the angles to show which angles are equal.

5 Now draw some pictures of your own. Each picture must have two parallel lines and two other lines.

Measure the angles of your pictures. Colour the angles to show which angles are equal.

Write about what you notice.

LETTERS OF THE ALPHABET

1 When two straight lines cross each other four angles are formed.

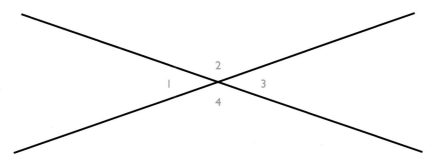

These four angles are not all different sizes. Measure each of the four angles. Which of the angles are equal?

2 Draw two straight lines crossing each other.

Measure each of the four angles. Colour the angles to show which angles are equal.

 Some letters of the alphabet, like Z, are made from straight lines.

Other letters, like B, have curved lines in them.

The letter Z has two parallel lines in it. So, two of the angles are equal. These angles have been coloured in red.

---

3 Draw all the letters of the alphabet which are made from straight lines.

Which of these letters have parallel lines in them?

Look at all the letters you have drawn. Colour in the equal angles.

 4 Use *Logo* to draw some of the letters of the alphabet.

5 Look at this picture.

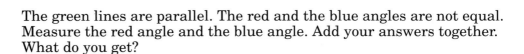

The green lines are parallel. The red and the blue angles are not equal. Measure the red angle and the blue angle. Add your answers together. What do you get?

6 Draw two parallel lines. Now draw a third line crossing them. Mark two angles which are *not* equal. Measure these angles. Add your answers.

Now start again with two more parallel lines.

Do this several times.

Write about what you find.

 **7** Draw a parallelogram using *Logo*.

BACK TO THE BEGINNING

This picture is almost the same as one of the pictures at the start of Task 21.

The only difference is that some of the lines have been extended. These lines are coloured red.

Measure the angles between the red lines and the blue lines.

Which of the blue lines are parallel?

G23
page
117

REVIEW EXERCISES G

EXERCISE 20   Units and measures

1   Which of these statements is sensible?

(*a*) The book is 21 cm wide.

(*b*) The pencil is 100 millimetres long.

(*c*) Alex is 3 metres tall.

(*d*) The classroom is 10 metres long.

(*e*) The classroom is 1000 millimetres high.

(*f*) This recipe says use 100g of butter.

(*g*) Sharon cycles 45 kilometres to school.

(*h*) James walks 200 metres to school.

2   Choose the correct answer.

(*a*) The tin of beans holds

400 grams   400 pounds
400 ounces   400 kilograms.

(*b*) A normal bottle of milk holds about

0.6 pints   0.6 litres   0.6 gallons.

(*c*) The time Gary took to write his name was

2 seconds   2 minutes
2 hours   2 days.

(*d*) David boiled the potatoes for

20 seconds   20 minutes
20 hours   20 days

(*e*) In an hour, Meena can walk

5 centimetres   5 inches
5 yards   5 metres
5 kilometres   5 miles

(*f*) A gallon of petrol is about

2 litres   5 litres
20 litres   50 litres

(*g*) A kilogram of sugar is about

2 ounces   8 ounces
2 pounds   8 pounds

3   Helen, Emma and Greco measured the same objects in the classroom. Here are Helen's measurements

pencil length 16 cm
computer screen width 33 cm
door width 77 cm
cube length 1.9 cm
ruler width 3.8 cm
room length 830 cm.

(*a*) Emma wrote her measurements in millimetres. What did she write?

(*b*) Greco wrote his measurements in metres. What did he write?

(*c*) What would you use? Would you use different units for different objects?

EXERCISE 21   Ratio

1   5 miles is roughly the same as 8 kilometres.

(*a*) How many kilometres is 15 miles?

(*b*) How many miles is 32 kilometres?

(*c*) How many miles is 20 kilometres?

2   2 pounds is roughly the same as 1 kilogram.

(a) Roughly how many pounds is 3 kilograms?

(b) Roughly how many kilograms is 8 pounds?

(*c*) Someone weighs 10 stone. Roughly how many kilograms is this?
(One stone is 14 pounds.)

3   One pound (£) is worth roughly 3 Deutschmarks (DM)

(*a*) How much is £10 worth in DM?

(*b*) How much is 60 DM worth in £?

(*c*) Someone changes £50 into DM, goes on holiday to Germany and spends 96 DM. At the end of the holiday she changes the DM back into £. Roughly how much does she get?

EXERCISE 22 Number patterns 2

1 Which of these numbers are cube numbers:
  8, 64, 100, 125, 225, 256, 512, 1000?

2 Which of these numbers are prime numbers?
  5, 9, 15, 19, 25, 29, 35, 39, 45, 49?

3 When 1 is added to a square number the answer is a prime number.

  What could the square number be?

4 When 1 is added to triangular number the answer is a square number.

  What could the triangular number be?

5 When a square number is added to a cube number the answer is a triangular number.

  What could the three numbers be?

6 (*a*) What are the factors of 32?

  (*b*) What are the factors of 243?

7 (*a*) Calculate $2 \times 3 \times 5$.

  (*b*) Find all the factors of your answer to (*a*).

  (*c*) Calculate $7 \times 11 \times 13$.

  (*d*) Find all the factors of your answer to (*c*).

8 7 and 11 are two prime numbers. What they are added the answer is 18.

  (*a*) Two prime number are added. The answer is 12. What are the numbers?

  (*b*) Two prime numbers are added. The answer is 45. What are the numbers?

  (*c*) Two prime numbers are multiplied. The answer ends in a 0. What are the numbers?

  (*d*) Two prime numbers are multiplied. The answer ends in 2. What could the numbers be?

  (*e*) Two prime numbers are multiplied. The answer ends in 3. Neither of the numbers end in 3. What could the numbers be?

EXERCISE 23 Parallel lines

1 Sketch these diagrams. Colour the equal angles the same colour.

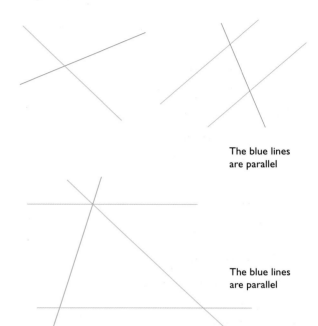

The blue lines are parallel

The blue lines are parallel

2 Sketch these diagrams. *Work out* the sizes of all the angles without using a protractor.

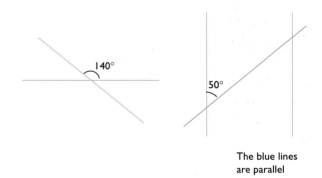

The blue lines are parallel

The blue lines are parallel

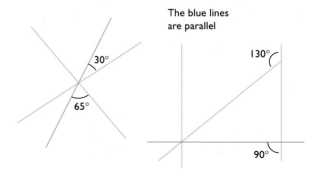

22 WHAT IS A THIRD?

a third $\frac{1}{3}$ 0.333333333333333 ...

A THIRD OF A NUMBER

A third of 6 is 2.
A third of 33 is 11.
A third of 27 is 9.

Make up some more sentences like this. Use small numbers in some of the sentences. Use large numbers in some of the sentences.

A THIRD OF A SHAPE

You need the resource sheet 'Thirds of shapes' for question 1.

You need squared paper or isometric paper for question 2.

 A **third** of each of these shapes is shaded.

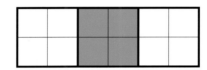 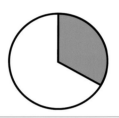

1 Look at the resource sheet.

Shade in a third of each shape. Do this as accurately as you can.

Some of the shapes are quite tricky!

2 Draw some shapes of your own. Shade a third of each of the shapes.

A THIRD OF A RECTANGLE

You need squared paper for this activity.

 This is a rectangle is of 9 squares by 6 squares.

The two pictures below show two different ways of shading a **third** of its area.

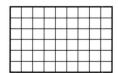

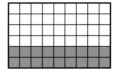 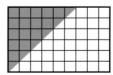

1 Draw some rectangles, 9 squares by 6 squares.

Shade a third of the area of each rectangle.
Shade each rectangle in a different way.

Show your drawings to someone else.
Ask them to pick a rectangle. Now convince them that a third of this rectangle has been shaded.

2 Draw several rectangles of a different size.
Shade a third of the area of each rectangle.

A THIRD FULL

1 Get an ice cream container. Fill it with something. You could use water or sand or rice, for example.

Now tip some out so that the container is a third full. Think of a way of doing this accurately. Draw carefully what the carton looks like when it is a third full.

2 Do the same with other containers. You could use:

a bowl
a cup
a milk bottle
a yogurt pot
a vase
or anything else.

0.333333....

1 Divide 1 by 3 on your calculator. Write down the answer you get. What answer would you get if you had a wider calculator?

Discuss this with someone else.

2 Divide 2 by 3 on your calculator. Write down the answer you get. What answer would you get if you had a wider calculator?

Discuss this with someone else.

3 Predict what answer you will get on your calculator if you divide
3 by 3.
And 4 by 3.
And 5 by 3.
And so on.

Now use a calculator to check your predictions.

4 Divide 2 by 3 on your calculator again. Look at the answer you get.

Now try to get the same answer by doing other sums on your calculator.

Find interesting ways of getting this answer.

PERCENTAGES

You need squared paper for this activity.

 Look at the square below. 1% of the square is shaded.

Now look at this picture. Half the square is shaded. This is 50% of the square.

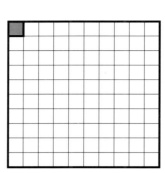

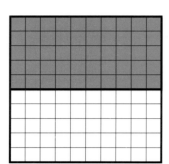

1   Draw a 10 by 10 square on squared paper. Shade a quarter of the square.

   What percentage of the square have you shaded?

   What percentage of the square have you not shaded?

2   Draw a 10 by 10 square. Now shade a fifth of the square. What percentage have you shaded?

   What percentage of the square have you not shaded?

3   Draw a 10 by 10 square. Now shade a third of the square. This is not so easy!

   What percentage of the square have you shaded?

   What percentage of the square have you not shaded?

4   Draw a rectangle on squared paper. Shade 50% of the rectangle.

5   Now draw another rectangle and shade 75% of it.

6   Now draw another rectangle and shade $\frac{1}{3}$ of it. What percentage of the rectangle have you shaded?

7   Which of these numbers is less than $\frac{1}{3}$?

   (a) 20%   (b) $\frac{1}{4}$ (c) $\frac{1}{2}$ (d) 40%   (e) 0.3

8   Which of these numbers is less than $\frac{2}{3}$?

   (a) 50%   (b) 75%   (c) 60%   (d) 0.6   (e) 0.7

9   Which of these numbers is more than $\frac{1}{3}$?

   (a) 0.33   (b) 0.34   (c) 0.335   (d) 0.333   (e) 0.3334

10 (*a*) Write down a decimal which is smaller than $\frac{2}{3}$ but very close to $\frac{2}{3}$.

(*b*) Write down a decimal which is larger than $\frac{2}{3}$ but very close to $\frac{2}{3}$.

(*c*) Write down a percentage which is larger than $\frac{2}{3}$ but very close to $\frac{2}{3}$.

MORE THAN A THIRD

Find out which of the following statements are true.

1 More than a third of the students in your class are girls.

2 More than a third of the students in your class are boys.

3 More than a third of the students in your class have an older brother or sister.

4 More than a third of the students in your class have a younger brother or sister.

5 More than a third of the teachers in your school are men.

6 More than a third of the teachers in your school are women.

7 More than a third of the classroom floor is covered by furniture.

8 More than a third of the classroom walls are windows.

9 When your class are all there they fill more than a third of the space in the classroom.

10 You spend more than a third of each school day at school.

11 You spend more than a third of each year at school.

12 You spend more than a third of your life asleep.

13 It is daylight for more than a third of the time at this time of year.

14 Each year, banks are closed on more than a third of the days.

15 Where you live more than a third of the days are wet.

23 IT'S MAGIC!

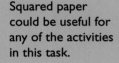

MAGIC SQUARES

Squared paper could be useful for any of the activities in this task.

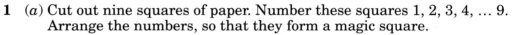

9		9	
1	9	2	12
8	3	7	18
4	6	5	15
13	18	14	

I Here is a square made from the numbers 1 to 9.

The red numbers are not part of the square. They show the total of the numbers

- in each row,
- in each column,
- and along each diagonal.

These totals are not all the same. If they were all the same the square would be called a **magic square.**

1 (a) Cut out nine squares of paper. Number these squares 1, 2, 3, 4, ... 9. Arrange the numbers, so that they form a magic square.

When you have made a magic square, keep a copy of how the numbers are arranged.

(b) Each of your rows, columns and diagonals should have the same total. What is this magic total?

(c) Now try to arrange the numbers in a different way to make a magic square.

How many different arrangements can you find?

2 Arrange the numbers 12, 13, 14, 15, 16, 17, 18, 19 and 20 to form a magic square.

What is the magic total?

3 Choose any nine *consecutive* numbers. Arrange them to form a magic square.

What is the magic total?

4 Here are nine numbers:

1, 7, 13, 31, 37, 43, 61, 67, 73

Arrange them so that they form a magic square.

What is the magic total?

5 Make a magic square from nine *different even* numbers.

6 Make a magic square from nine *different odd* numbers.

7 Make a magic square using these seven numbers and two others.

8, 10, 11, 13, 15, 16, 18

Now try again, but do not use the same two extra numbers as last time.

You could choose 7, 8, 9, 10, 11, 12, 13, 14, 15.
Or 36, 37 ... 44
Or 3465, 3466 ... 3473

TAKE THREE NUMBERS

Here is a magic square made using just three different numbers.

5	9	7
9	7	5
7	5	9

1 Make a different magic square using these three numbers.

2 Choose three numbers of your own. Try to make a magic square from them.

Write about anything you notice.

ZERO TOTAL SQUARES

This is a zero total magic square.

−2	5	−3
−1	0	1
3	−5	2

1 What does zero total mean?

2 Make a zero total square using these numbers:

−4, −3, −2, −1, 0, 1, 2, 3, 4

3 Make a zero total magic square using a different set of nine numbers.

4 Make a zero total magic square using nine even numbers.

Magic squares have fascinated people for a long while. The ancient Chinese knew about magic squares.

H25 page 137

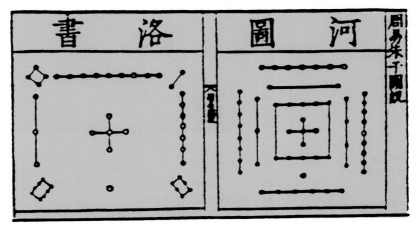

123

4 BY 4 MAGIC SQUARES

Albrecht Dürer produced a picture in 1514.

The picture contained this magic square.

16	3	2	13
5	10	11	8
9	6	7	12
4	15	14	1

1   Check that this square is magic.

2   You can produce a different magic square by swopping the first row and the last row. Here is the square you get.

4	15	14	1
5	10	11	8
9	6	7	12
16	3	2	13

Try swopping other pairs of rows.

Try swopping pairs of columns.

Sometimes you still get a magic square.

Sometimes you don't!

How many different magic squares can you make in this way?

Write about anything you notice.

 Here is a different way of making a new magic square.
Take Dürer's square and rotate it through a right angle.

4	9	5	16
15	6	10	3
14	7	11	2
1	12	8	13

You can adjust the numbers, so that they are upright again!

You can also try reflecting a magic square in a mirror.

3   See how many different 4 by 4 magic squares you can find using the idea in the box above.

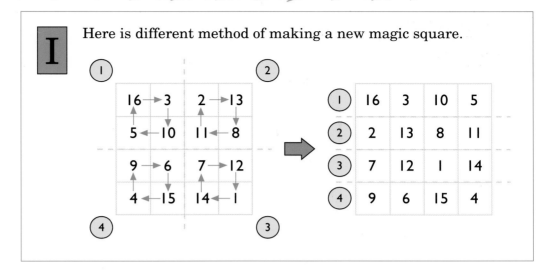

Here is different method of making a new magic square.

4   Try using this method on this magic square:

6	3	10	15
16	9	4	5
11	14	7	2
1	8	13	12

Now try changing the method a bit. See if your changed method still produces magic squares.

JOINING CONSECUTIVE NUMBERS

Choose a magic square. Join the numbers up in order, like this.

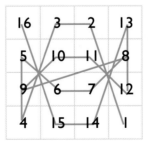

Now try it with a different magic square. Do you get the same pattern of lines, or a different pattern?

Try this with several squares. Write about what you discover.

ODD ORDER MAGIC SQUARES

 An **odd order** magic square means a 3 by 3 square, a 5 by 5 square, a 7 by 7 square and so on.

Here is a method of making a 7 by 7 magic square.

First write out the numbers 1 to 49 in a diamond shape (see figure 1).

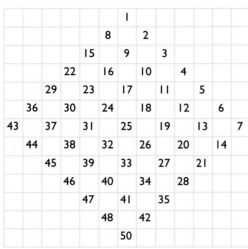

Figure 1

Figure 2

Now draw the outline of the finished square (see figure 2).

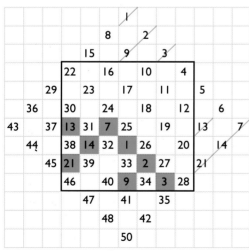

Now move the outside numbers into the outline. Move them up or down or across. Look at figure 3 to see how to do it.

Figure 3

1 Use the method shown to make a 5 by 5 magic square.

> You do not have to use the numbers 1 to 25 in a 5 by 5 magic square.
> You could, for example, start with the numbers shown in Figure 4.

		4		
	8		7	
	12	11		10
16	15	14	13	
20	19	18	17	16
	23	22	21	20
	26	25	24	
		29	28	
		32		

Figure 4

2 Complete the magic square using the numbers in figure 4. What is the magic total for this square?

3 Now experiment with numbers of your own. You cannot just use any numbers. They have to obey the same rules as the numbers in figure 4. What do you think these rules are? You can experiment to find out.

4 Construct a 9 by 9 magic square.
Or an 11 by 11 magic square.
Or …

A DIFFERENT METHOD FOR MAKING A 5 BY 5 SQUARE

1 First copy figure 5

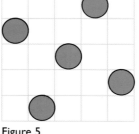

Figure 5

2 Now put any number between 1 and 5 in the ringed squares. It does not have to be 2.

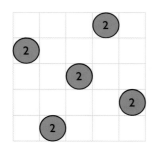

3 Now fill the top row with the other numbers between 1 and 5. These numbers can be in *any* order.

3	1	5	(2)	4
(2)				
		(2)		
			(2)	
	(2)			

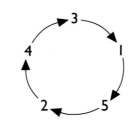

4 Now fill the other rows with the other numbers. You must put them in the same order as in the first row.

3	1	5	(2)	4
(2)	4	3	1	5
1	5	(2)	4	3
4	3	1	5	(2)
5	(2)	4	3	1

5 Now copy figure 6.

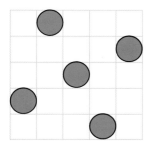

Figure 6

6 Now do the same as before, but use the numbers 0, 5, 10, 15 and 20. It does not matter which number goes in the rings.

5	(15)	10	0	20
10	0	20	5	(15)
20	5	(15)	10	0
(15)	10	0	20	5
0	20	5	(15)	10

7 Now add your two squares together. This will produce a magic square.

8	16	15	2	24
12	4	23	6	20
21	10	17	14	3
19	13	1	25	7
5	22	9	18	11

8 Now make other magic squares using different numbers in the rings and different orders for the other numbers.

COLOURING MAGIC SQUARES

Choose a magic square and colour it. Colour the odd numbers with one colour. Colour the even numbers with a different colour.

8	16	15	2	24
12	4	23	6	20
21	10	17	14	3
19	13	1	25	7
5	22	9	18	11

Do you get a symmetrical pattern? What kind of symmetry does it have?

Try colouring other magic squares in this way.

Invent your own rules for deciding how to colour magic squares.

3	20	7	24	11
22	14	1	18	10
9	21	13	5	17
16	8	25	12	4
15	2	19	6	23

MAGIC CROSSES

Here is a magic cross.

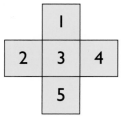

1 Rearrange the numbers 1, 2, 3, 4 and 5 to make a different magic cross.

How many different arrangements can you find?

What is the biggest magic total you can make?

What is the smallest?

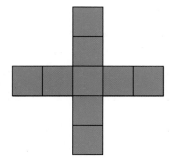

2 Here is a different grid for a magic cross. Arrange the numbers 1 to 9 in it to make it magic.

How many different magic totals are possible?

3 Make magic crosses using a different set of nine numbers. Write about what you find.

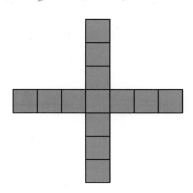

4 Try other sizes of magic cross.
Write about what you find.

5 Invent other magic shapes.
Investigate them.

A DIFFERENT KIND OF MAGIC

1 Here is a square with a new type of magic.

256	2	64
8	32	128
16	512	4

New magic (version 1)

What sort of magic does this square have?

2 Place these numbers into a square which is magic in the same way:

1, 2, 3, 4, 6, 9, 12, 18, 36

Now use these numbers instead:

1, 3, 5, 9, 15, 25, 45, 75, 225

New magic (version 2)

I	8 is called a **power** of 2. This is because $$8 = 2 \times 2 \times 2 = 2^3.$$ 81 is a power of 3, because $$81 = 3 \times 3 \times 3 \times 3 = 3^4.$$

3 (*a*) Look again at the square labelled 'New magic (version 1)'.
All the numbers in this square are powers of 2.

Copy and complete the square labelled 'New magic (version 2)'
to show all the numbers as powers of 2.

(*b*) What is the connection between the square you have just
completed and the magic squares in the first activity (on page 122)?

4 Make a different magic square with this new kind of magic. It should
contain the numbers 1, 3, 9, 27, 81 and four other numbers.

H25 page 137

5 Make another magic square with this new kind of magic. You could
make it so that all the numbers end with the same digit.

24 PEOPLE AND CALCULATORS

DIFFERENT WAYS OF WRITING NUMBERS

1 What different ways of writing numbers do you know?

 Roman numbers

I	1	C	100	CCXXXVI means 236
V	5	D	500	CX means 110 but
X	10	M	1000	XC means 90
L	50			

2 (*a*) Here is a Roman clock face.

What time does it show?

(*b*) Here is a mile stone. The Roman number at the bottom of the stone tells you when the stone was put there.

Which year was the stone put there?

3 When were you born? Write this as a Roman number. When will you be 40? Write this as a Roman number.

 The numerals we normally use in Britain are called **Hindu-Arabic numerals.**

The same numerals are used to write many different numbers.

For example, the numerals 2 and 7 are all that are needed to write these numbers

2, 7, 22, 27, 77.

4 How many different numbers less than 1000 can be written using *only* the numerals 2 and 7?

 The Hindu-Arabic system is widely used. But different people use different characters for the digits. Here are the first ten numbers written in Gujarati:

Here are the first six multiples of ૪

5 (a) Write down the first six multiples of **২**

(b) Write down the first six multiples of **৪**

6 These calculations are written in Bengali. Look at them carefully. See if you can discover what they mean.

(a) **৫ + ৫ = ১০**

(b) **৫ + ৫ + ৫ + ৫ = ২০**

(c) **৮ × ৮ = ৬৪**

(d) **৪ × ৪ × ৪ = ৬৪**

QUICK METHODS WITH WHOLE NUMBERS

People are not the same as calculators and computers. Calculators use set methods to get answers. People use many different methods.

Find the answers to these without a calculator:

1 (a)
$$4 + 9$$
$$40 + 90$$
$$400 + 900$$
$$399 + 900$$
$$399 + 899$$

(b)
$$5 \times 7$$
$$50 \times 7$$
$$49 \times 7$$
$$50 \times 70$$
$$49 \times 70$$

2 (a)
$$56 - 20 \qquad 63 - 30 \qquad 94 - 50$$
$$56 - 19 \qquad 63 - 29 \qquad 94 - 49$$

(b)
$$37 - 20 \qquad 77 - 40 \qquad 86 - 60$$
$$37 - 18 \qquad 77 - 38 \qquad 86 - 58$$

3 (a)
$$4 \times 40 \qquad 3 \times 50 \qquad 5 \times 30$$
$$4 \times 42 \qquad 3 \times 53 \qquad 5 \times 33$$

(b)
$$6 \times 60 \qquad 7 \times 40 \qquad 9 \times 90$$
$$6 \times 64 \qquad 7 \times 42 \qquad 9 \times 94$$

(c) $5 \times 53 \quad 3 \times 64 \quad 4 \times 76 \quad 6 \times 39 \quad 8 \times 44 \quad 9 \times 37$

4 (a)
$$2 \times 15$$
$$4 \times 15$$
$$8 \times 15$$
$$16 \times 15$$

(b)
$$3 \times 32$$
$$6 \times 32$$
$$12 \times 32$$
$$24 \times 32$$

(c)
$$16 \times 37$$
$$24 \times 43$$
$$14 \times 14$$
$$36 \times 63$$

5 (a)
$$6 \times 6 \qquad 10 \times 10 \qquad 20 \times 20 \qquad 100 \times 100$$
$$5 \times 7 \qquad 9 \times 11 \qquad 19 \times 21 \qquad 99 \times 101$$

(b)
$$6 \times 6 \qquad 10 \times 10 \qquad 30 \times 30 \qquad 400 \times 400$$
$$4 \times 8 \qquad 8 \times 12 \qquad 28 \times 32 \qquad 398 \times 402$$

QUICK METHODS WITH DECIMALS

1 (a) 5.6 − 2   6.3 − 3   9.4 − 5
         5.6 − 1.9   6.3 − 2.9   9.4 − 4.9

   (b) 3.7 − 2   7.7 − 4   8.6 − 6
        3.7 − 1.8   7.7 − 3.8   8.6 − 5.8

2 (a) 4 × 4   3 × 5   5 × 3
        4 × 4.2   3 × 5.3   5 × 3.3

   (b) 6 × 6   7 × 4   9 × 9
        6 x 6.4   7 × 4.2   9 × 9.4

   (c) 5 × 5.3   3 × 6.4   4 × 7.6   6 × 3.9   8 × 4.4   9 × 0.37

3 (a)   2 × 1.5   (b)   3 × 3.2   (c)   1.6 × 3.7
          4 × 1.5   6 × 3.2   2.4 × 4.3
          8 × 0.15   12 × 3.2   1.4 × 1.4
         16 × 0.15   24 × 0.32   0.36 × 6.3

METHODS FOR ADDING

1 (a) Without using a calculator work out 345 + 428.
   (b) Explain the method you used to other people.

2 Here is one method which people use for addition.

$$
\begin{array}{r}
245 \\
+\,377 \\
\hline
500 \\
110 \\
12 \\
\hline
622
\end{array}
$$

Try this method. Decide whether you like it.

METHODS FOR SUBTRACTING

1 (*a*) Without using a calculator work out 623 − 457.

   (*b*) Explain the method you used to other people.

2 Here are two methods which people use for subtraction.

$$
\begin{array}{r}
563 \\
-287 \\
\hline
3\overline{2}\overline{4} \\
\hline
276
\end{array}
$$

$$
\begin{array}{rl}
563 \rightarrow & 563 \\
-287 \rightarrow & +712 \quad (999-287=712)\\
& +275 \\
& \underline{+1} \\
& 276
\end{array}
$$

Discuss these methods with other people. Make sure you understand how to use them.
Try them out. Decide whether you like them.

METHODS FOR MULTIPLYING

1 (*a*) Without using a calculator work out 46 × 37.

   (*b*) Explain the method you used to other people.

2 This method is called *Russian peasant multiplication*. Here it is used to calculate 73 × 58.

$$
\begin{array}{rl}
73 & \times\ 58 \\
\cancel{36} & \cancel{116} \\
\cancel{18} & \cancel{232} \\
9 & 464 \\
\cancel{4} & \cancel{928} \\
\cancel{2} & \cancel{1856} \\
1 & 3712.+ \\
\hline
& 4234
\end{array}
$$

(halve and double)

Discuss this method with other people.
Make sure you understand how to use it.
Try it out. Decide whether you like it.

METHODS FOR DIVIDING

1 (a) Without using a calculator work out 962 ÷ 26.

   (b) Explain the method you used to other people.

2 Here is one method which some people use for division. Here it is used to calculate 800 ÷ 23.

```
                    800
20 × 23             460 −
                    ─────
                    340
10 × 23             230 −
                    ─────
                    110
4 × 23               92 −        800 ÷ 23 = 34 remainder 18
────                ─────
34                   18
```

H25
page
137

Discuss this method with other people. Make sure you understand how to use it.

Try this method. Decide whether you like it.

DOUBLING AND HALVING WITH A CALCULATOR

Calculators do not use quick or unusual methods of calculating. But people can use the answers calculators give to discover patterns and relationships between numbers which calculators will never know about.

1 (a) Use a calculator to double these numbers:

       2358, 4229, 7400, 63236.

   (b) Choose some more numbers to double.

2 What happens to numbers when you double them?

   (a) What happens to the number of digits?

   (b) What happens to the number of zeros at the end?

3 Use your calculator to double these numbers:

       9, 99, 999, 9999, …

   There is a pattern to the answers. Keep going until your calculator breaks the pattern! What does your calculator do?

4 (a) Treble some numbers.
   (b) What happens to the number of digits this time?
   (c) What happens to the number of zeros at the end?

5 Halve some big numbers.

   Write about anything you notice.

SMALL CALCULATORS

TX 120

I These are the answers produced by an (imaginary) small calculator.

A   36 + 57 =   **93**   B   6345 – 3246 =   **3099**

C   53 × 35 =   **1855**   D   5467 + 6324 =   **E**

E   101 × 99 =   **9999**   F   223 × 97 =   **E**

G   3.6 + 2.7 =   **6.3**   H   3.6 × 2.7 =   **9.72**

I   6.8 × 5.4 =   **36.7**   J   4.3 × 4.6 =   **19.8**

K   10 ÷ 3 =   **3.33**   L   5 ÷ 3 =   **1.67**

---

1 (a) Check all these calculations using your own calculator.

(b) Why does the small calculator give **E** as the answer to two of the calculations?

(c) Look carefully at *I, J, K* and *L*. Make sure you understand how the small calculator gets its answers.

2 What would the small calculator give as the answers to the following?

(a) 164 + 236 (b) 2000 – 432

(c) 42 × 24 (d) 1234 + 8765

(e) 8765 + 4321 (f) 123 × 97

(g) 4.9 + 5.8 (h) 5.9 × 4.8

(i) 6.3 × 7.6 (j) 10.4 × 12.6

(k) 40 ÷ 7 (l) 40 ÷ 13

H24
page
136

REVIEW EXERCISES H

EXERCISE 24 Fractions, decimals and percentages

1 Someone counted 50 cars. 24% of them were red.

(a) How many cars were red?

(b) What percentage were not red?

2 There are 25 children in a class. 64% of them are girls.

(a) How many are girls?

(b) What percentage are boys?

3 $\frac{1}{4}$ of the students in a class wear glasses. What percentage do not wear glasses?

4 80% of the students in a school walk to school. What fraction of the students do not walk to school?

5 Pick out the biggest from each pair.

(a) $\frac{1}{2}$ and 80%   (d) $\frac{1}{3}$ and 50%

(b) $\frac{1}{4}$ and 20%   (e) $\frac{2}{3}$ and 70%

(c) $\frac{3}{4}$ and 100%   (f) $\frac{1}{6}$ and 15%

6 Pick out the biggest from each pair.

(a) $\frac{1}{2}$ and $\frac{3}{4}$ (d) $\frac{1}{2}$ and $\frac{1}{3}$

(b) $\frac{1}{3}$ and $\frac{2}{3}$ (e) $\frac{1}{4}$ and $\frac{1}{3}$

(c) $\frac{2}{5}$ and $\frac{3}{5}$ (f) $\frac{2}{3}$ and $\frac{3}{4}$

7 Pick out the biggest from each pair.

(a) $\frac{1}{4}$ and 0.4   (d) $\frac{2}{5}$ and 0.5

(b) $\frac{1}{5}$ and 0.5   (e) $\frac{1}{5}$ and 0.15

(c) $\frac{1}{3}$ and 0.3   (f) $\frac{1}{8}$ and 0.18

8 What is the nearest whole number to

(a) 3.2?   (d) 4.093?

(b) 5.8?   (e) 2.55?

(c) 6.19?   (f) −4.8?

9 Write down three numbers between

(a) 4 and 5   (c) 3.2 and 3.3

(b) 7.5 and 8   (d) 6.5 and 6.51

10 0.25 is exactly the same as a quarter. Which of the following are **exact?**

(a) 0.75 is the same as $\frac{3}{4}$.

(b) 0.6 is the same as $\frac{3}{5}$.

(c) 0.33 is the same as $\frac{1}{3}$.

(d) 0.125 is the same as $\frac{1}{8}$.

(e) 0.555 is the same as $\frac{5}{9}$.

(f) 0.6666667 is the same as $\frac{2}{3}$.

(g) 0.7 is the same as $\frac{71}{100}$.

(h) 0.3125 is the same as $\frac{5}{16}$.

11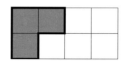

Which of these statements is closest to the truth?

(a) $\frac{1}{2}$ of the shape is shaded.

(b) 30% of the shape is shaded.

(c) 0.4 of the shape is shaded.

(d) $\frac{3}{5}$ of the shape is shaded.

12

Which of these statements is closest to the truth?

(a) $\frac{1}{7}$ of the shape is shaded.

(b) 70% of the shape is shaded.

(c) 0.77 of the shape is shaded.

(d) $\frac{4}{5}$ of the shape is needed.

13 A savings account pays 8% interest each year.
Sabrina puts £50 into her account. How much interest does she get after one year?

14 VAT is charged on a car service at 17.5%. Before the tax is added the bill is £60. What is the total bill after the tax is added?

EXERCISE 25 Without a calculator

1 Work out

(a) 7 + 9

(b) 70 + 90

(c) 0.7 + 0.9

(d) 700 + 9

2 Work out

(a) 100 − 70

(b) 100 − 36

(c) 100 − 55

(d) 1000 − 200

(e) 1000 − 420

(f) 1000 − 365

3 Work out

(a) 2 × 4

(b) 2 × 40

(c) 20 × 40

(d) 200 × 40

4 Work out

(a) 3 × 6

(b) 6 × 6

(c) 12 × 6

(d) 24 × 6

5 (a) How many weeks are 21 days?

(b) How many weeks and days are 25 days?

(c) How many weeks and days are 50 days?

(d) How many weeks and days are 100 days?

6 (a) How many days are 72 hours?

(b) How many days are 720 hours?

(c) How many days are 288 hours?

7 12 × 14 = 168

Work out

(a) 120 × 14

(b) 1200 × 14

(c) 120 × 140

(d) 12 × 1.4

(e) 1.2 × 1.4

(f) 12 × 13

8 28 × 36 = 1008

(a) What is 280 × 36?

(b) What is 28 × 37?

(c) What is 56 × 36?

(d) What is 56 × 72?

(e) Is 2.8 × 36 more or less than 100?

9 Here is a number machine.

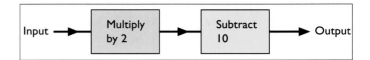

If the input is 2 the output is −6.

(a) What is the output if the input is 6?

(b) What is the output if the input is 3?

(c) What is the output if the input is 0?

(d) What input gives 10 as the output?

(e) What input gives −8 as the output?

(f) What input gives 0 as the output?

10 7 × 11 × 13 = 1001

(a) What is 1001 ÷ 13?

(b) What is 1001 ÷ 11?

(c) What is 1001 ÷ 7?

(d) Which is bigger: 0.7 × 1.1 × 1.3 or 1?

(e) What is 347 × 7 × 11 × 13?

11 Calculate:

(a) $2^2 \times 5^2$

(b) $2^3 \times 5^3$

(c) $2^4 \times 5^4$

(d) Write a million as $2^{\square} \times 5^{\square}$.

12 Calculate:

(a) 4^2 (b) 4^3 (c) 4^4 (d) 4^5

(e) What digit does 4^{10} end in?

(f) What digit does 4^{15} end in?

■ (g) What digit does 5^{15} end in?

25 WHAT IS A CIRCLE?

CIRCULAR OBJECTS

Find some circles in the classroom.

Find some circles at home.

Here are some objects which are circular.

1 What is a circle?

2 Look at the objects you have found and the objects in the photographs.

Why are they circular?

- Think about how they are made.
- Think about what they are used for.

MEASURING CIRCLES

 I A **diameter** of a circle is a line crossing the circle and going through the centre.

A diameter is longer than any other line you can draw across a circle.

1 (a) Find as many circles as possible.

Measure the diameter of each circle.

(b) Write out a list of the circles in order of size, starting with the smallest.

CIRCUMFERENCE

>
>
> The perimeter of a circle means the distance all round the circle. The perimeter of a circle is usually called the **circumference.**
>
> One way of finding the circumference of a circular object is to use a piece of string or a strip of paper.
>
> Another way is to mark a point on the circumference. You can then roll the circle until it has turned round once.

1 Measure the circumference of each of your circles.

Record your results in a table like this.

Object	Diameter	Circumference
Tin Wheel 10 p	10 cm	31 cm

2 A tin and a jar both have circular tops.

The diameter of the tin is the same as the diameter of the jar.

What can you say about the circumference of the tin and the circumference of the jar?

3 Look at the results in your table for question 3.

(*a*) A circle has a diameter of 10 cm. Estimate its circumference.

(*b*) A circle has a diameter of 15 cm. Estimate its circumference.

(*c*) A circle has a circumference of 18 cm. Estimate its diameter..

(*d*) A circle has a circumference of 60 cm. Estimate its diameter.

4 Copy and complete these statements.

The *circumference* of a circle is about _ _ _ times its *diameter.*

To get the *circumference* from the *diameter* you multiply by _ _ _.

To get the *diameter* from the *circumference* you divide by _ _ _.

CIRCLES EVERYWHERE

1 The diameter of a mat is 10 cm. A fly walks all round the edge of the mat. How far does the fly walk?

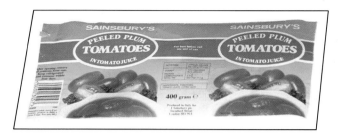

2 A tin has a diameter of 75 mm. There is a label stuck all round the side of the tin.

How long is the label?

3 A garden pond is circular. The distance round the pond is 24 m. Two people stand on the edge of the pond. They are as far away from each other as possible.

What is the distance between them?

4 A circular running track is 400 m long.

What is the diameter of the track?

I The **radius** of a circle is a line drawn from the centre to the outside.

The *radius* is *half* the *diameter*.
The *diameter* is *twice* the *radius*.

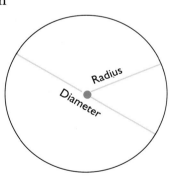

---

5 A goat is tethered to a post by a rope. The length of the rope is 5 m.

The goat walks round the post. It keeps as far from the post as possible.

How far has it walked when it is back where it started?

6 (*a*) The diameter of a wheel on a girl's bicycle is 60 cm. How far does the bicycle move when the wheel goes round once?

(*b*) The girl cycles to school each morning. The distance to school is 800 metres.

How many times does the bicycle wheel turn round?

7 Find the total length of the lines that mark this indoor hockey pitch.

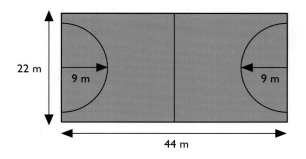

8 A trundle wheel moves forward 1 metre every time the wheel turns round once.

What is the radius of the wheel?

9 The diameter of a cotton reel is 3 cm. The length of the cotton on the reel is 91 m. How many times does the cotton wrap round the reel?

10 The Earth is always about 92 million miles from the Sun.

The Earth goes in a complete circle round the Sun each year.

(a) How far does the Earth travel in a year?

(b) What is the speed of the Earth in miles per second?

 Here is a *Logo* instruction which draws a circle.

```
REPEAT 90 [FD 8 RT 4]
```

1 Try out this instruction on a computer.

2 What happens if you change the instruction?
- You could change the blue number.
- You could change the red numbers.

I You can find the diameter of a *Logo* circle by finding how far you need to move the turtle to get across the circle.

3 (a) Find the circumference of each of your *Logo* circles.

(b) Find the diameter of each of your circles.

(c) How many times bigger is the circumference than the diameter for each of your circles?

4 Use *Logo* to draw a circle inside a square.

5 Use *Logo* to draw a square inside a circle.

π

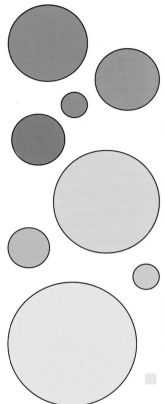

I Circles are all the same shape. This means that all circles look exactly the same. The only difference between different circles is their size.

If you know the diameter of *any* circle you can find the circumference. You do this by multiplying the diameter by about 3.

The exact number to multiply by is not 3. It is 3.1415926 … Circles are very important shapes. So, this exact number has been given a special name. It is called π. π (pronounced pi) is one of the letters in the Greek alphabet.

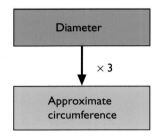

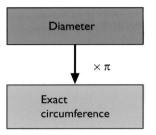

For practical problems 3 is often accurate enough to use. If it is not accurate enough, you can use 3.1, or even 3.14.

1 A circle has a diameter of 4 metres. Find the circumference of the circle as accurately as possible.

2 A circular paddling pool has a diameter of 1.5 m.

You might be able to use the π button on your calculator

126 page 162

    (*a*) Find the circumference of the paddling pool, as accurately as possible.

    (*b*) Why is your answer for (*a*) very silly?

    (*c*) Give a sensible answer for the circumference of the paddling pool.

HIDDEN CIRCLES

I Here are the names of some solid shapes.

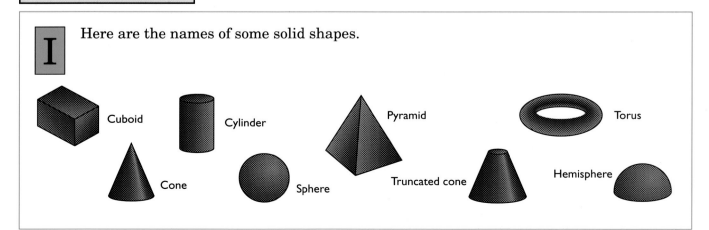

1 Look at the objects in the picture. Name the shape of each object.

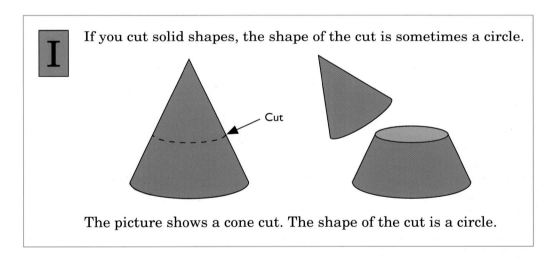

I If you cut solid shapes, the shape of the cut is sometimes a circle.

Cut

The picture shows a cone cut. The shape of the cut is a circle.

2 Which of these objects can be cut to produce circles? Which objects can be cut to produce circles of different sizes?

(a) Cylinder

(b) Cuboid

(c) Cone

(d) Pyramid

(e) Truncated cone

(f) Sphere

(g) Torus

(h) Hemisphere

CIRCLE PATTERNS

Draw some circle patterns. Here are some ideas.

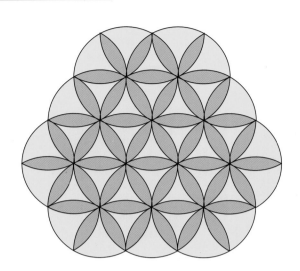
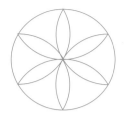
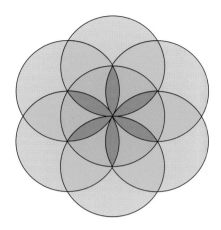

(i) Circles all the same size.

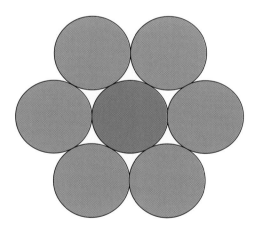

(ii) Circles of two sizes.

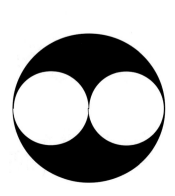
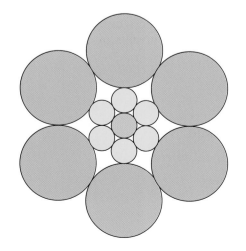
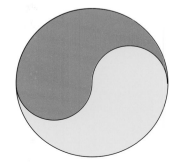

(iii) Concentric circles and diameters.

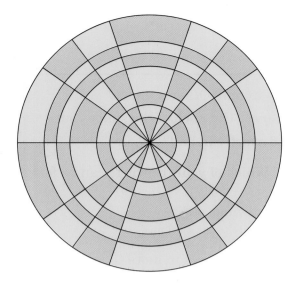

(iv) Circles through one point.

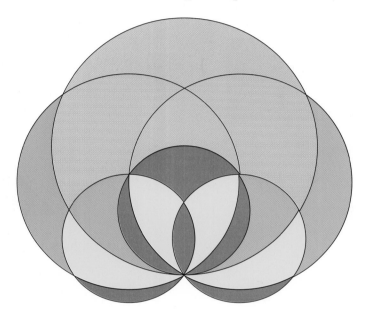

(v) Concentric circles and parallel lines.

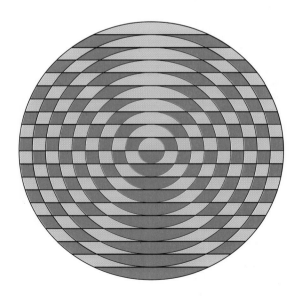

(vi) Touching circles.

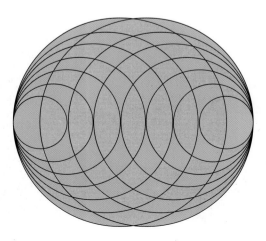

26 FOLDING PAPER AND CARD

FOLDING EXACTLY IN HALF

1 Some shapes can be folded exactly in half. Others cannot.

Use the resource sheet called *'Shapes'*. Cut each of the shapes out.

Which of the shapes can be folded exactly in half?

2 Find some objects to draw round. Which of your drawings can be folded exactly in half?

Try to decide *without* cutting the drawings out.

For this activity you need the resource sheet *'Shapes'*.

 Some shapes can be folded exactly in half in more than one way.

A square can be folded to give either this

or this

You might want to try this for yourself.

You might want to do question 3 without cutting out the shapes.

3 Each of these shapes can be folded exactly in half in more than one way.

Draw a sketch to show the different ways for each shape.

4 (*a*) When a particular shape is folded exactly in half, A is produced.

What was the shape? There is more than one answer.

(*b*) What shapes can be folded in half to get B, C, D and E?

In some cases there is more than one answer.

A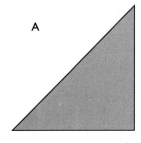

F19
page
99

B

C

D

E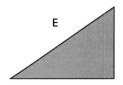

MOUNTAINS AND VALLEYS

For this activity you need some strips of paper.

1 Take a strip of paper. Fold it in half and half again.

Now unfold it. Look at the creases.

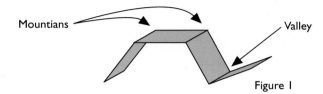

Mountains   Valley

Figure 1

Some of the creases are *'valleys'* and some of them are *'mountains'*.

The pattern in figure 1 (from left to right) could be written like this:

MMV

You could turn the strip over. If you did, you would get this fold pattern:

VVM

Explain why.

What fold pattern would you get if you turned the strip round?

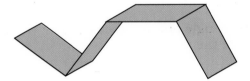

2 Take a strip of paper. Fold it in half three times.

Depending on how you do it you might get this fold pattern:

MVVVMMV

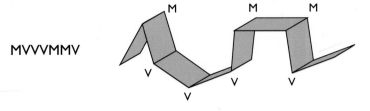

What other fold patterns can you get when folding three times?

3 Fold a strip in half four times. Write down the fold patterns you get.

Do it again in a different way. How many different fold patterns can you find?

127 page 162

MAKING A TETRAHEDRON

For this activity you need a piece of card.

Here is a way of making a tetrahedron. You need a rectangle of card 22 cm by 3 cm.

You need to draw lines on the card like this.

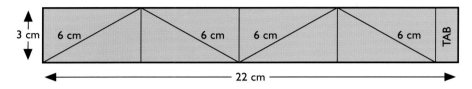

You use a compass to tell you where to draw the lines.

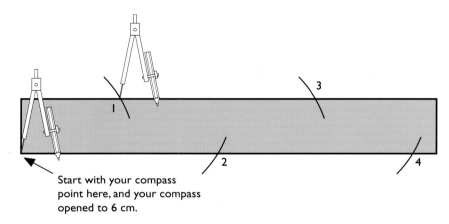

Start with your compass point here, and your compass opened to 6 cm.

Cut the rectangle out and crease along the lines. Stick the tab to the other end of the strip.

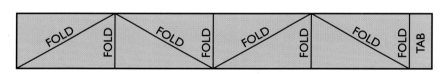

All folds are mountain folds.

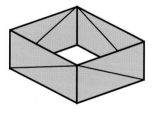

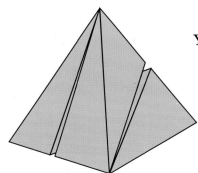

You should be able to bend your strip into a tetrahedron.

MAKING A DECORATION

This is a table decoration for Christmas.

When this decoration is opened out it is this shape.

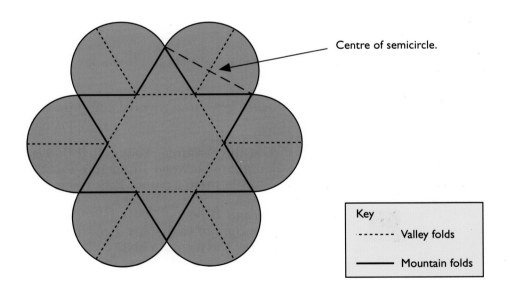

Centre of semicircle.

Key

------- Valley folds

——— Mountain folds

1 Make a table decoration like this.

2 The decoration described is based on a hexagon. Make a similar decoration based on a square. Or a pentagon. Or an octagon. Or …

3 Explore your own ideas for decorations you can make by folding paper or card.

27 NUMBER LADDERS

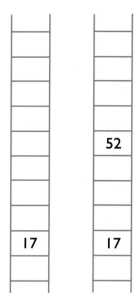

Here is a game you can play. It is called ladders. Each player will need to draw a 'ladder' of 10 boxes.

- One person is in charge of the game. This person can call out any whole number between 1 and 100. When the number is called, you write it in one of the boxes on your ladder.

- Suppose the first person calls out 17. You put 17 in one of the boxes.

- You are not allowed to change the place for the number after you have written it.

- The person in charge then calls out another number. Suppose it is 52. You can choose which box to put 52 in, but 52 *must* be above 17.

- You can only write *one* number in each box.

- The person in charge keeps calling out numbers. You put each number onto your ladder *if you can*.

The winner is the person who fills the ladder first.

CHOOSING THE NUMBERS FAIRLY

I The fairest way to play is for the numbers to be chosen by chance.

Here are three ways of doing this.

First Way
Get the resource sheet called *'100 square'*. Cut out each of the numbers between 1 and 100. Put the numbers in a box or bag. Shuffle them around. Pick them out one by one.

Second Way
Get *Spread* to display 1 row and 1 column.
Enter the formula RND (100)
Keep pressing U to get the numbers.

Third Way
Use a graphical calculator or any other calculator with a random number button.

On a Casio graphical calculator you can enter this:

| Int | (| Ran # | × | 1 | 0 | 0 |) |

You then keep pressing the EXE button to get the numbers.

PLAYING THE GAME

Play the game of ladders. You could play in small groups, or with the whole class.

The person in charge needs to decide how the numbers will be chosen.

YOU COULD USE:

You could use the computer program *Ladders* to play ladders.

The computer is in charge. The computer chooses the numbers by chance. You play on your own. At the end the computer tells you how many numbers it needed to choose, so that you could fill *all* your boxes.

WHAT IF?

What if the 'ladder' has a different number of boxes?

All the players could decide to use a ladder with just 5 boxes.

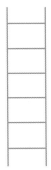

The person in charge still calls out numbers between 1 and 100.

1 (*a*) Suppose the first number called out was 42. Where would you put this number? Why?

   (*b*) Where would you put 42, if the ladder had 6 boxes?

   (*c*) What if the ladder had 7 boxes? 8 boxes? … 20 boxes?

2 Repeat question 1, but use another number instead of 42.

3 Discuss your answers to questions 1 and 2 with someone else.

   If your answers are different see if you can come to an agreement.

USING DECIMALS

The normal game of ladders uses whole numbers between 1 and 100.

You could use decimal numbers between 0 and 10 instead.

I To get decimal numbers between 0 and 10 using *Spread,* you could enter this formula:

A = RND (1000)/100

To get decimal numbers between 0 and 10 using a graphical calculator you could use

Int (Ran # × 1 0 0) ÷ 1 0

You could use the *'Ladders'* program.

1 Play ladders with 10 boxes, using decimal numbers between 0 and 10.

2 Play ladders with these numbers, but using ladders with a different number of boxes.

3 Suppose you are using a ladder with 5 boxes. Suppose the first number is 6.43. Where would you put this number?

Where would you put 6.43, if you were using 6 boxes? 7 boxes? …

4 Play ladders using a different set of decimal numbers.

USING NEGATIVE NUMBERS

You could use negative numbers for ladders.

I To get whole numbers between –20 and 20 using *Spread,* you could enter this formula:

A = RND (40) – 20

To get whole numbers between –20 and 20 using a graphical calculator you could use

Int (Ran # × 4 0) – 2 0

You could use the *'Ladders'* program.

1 Play ladders with 10 boxes, using whole numbers between –20 and 20.

2 Play ladders with these numbers, but using ladders with a different number of boxes.

3 Suppose you are using a ladder with 5 boxes. Suppose the first number is –7. Where would you put this number?

Where would you put –7, if you were using 6 boxes? 7 boxes? …

128 page 163

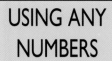

USING ANY NUMBERS

Here is another version of ladders.

The person who chooses the numbers does not tell the players what types of numbers are being used. The players have to work this out for themselves.

• Play this version of ladders.

Play it more than once, so that the players can begin to realise what types of numbers are being used.

TAKING TURNS TO CHOOSE THE NUMBERS

Here is another version of ladders.

There is no special person to choose the numbers. Instead, players take turns to choose a number which suits them. All the other players have to use this number as well.

• Play this version of ladders, where each player takes a turn to choose a number.

What advice would you give to someone playing this game?

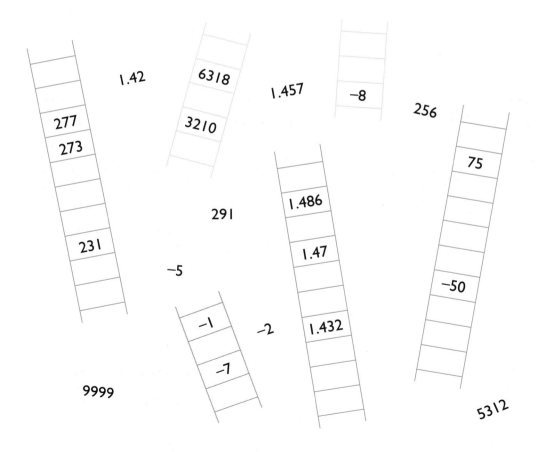

28 WHAT A LOAD OF RUBBISH!

What day of the week is rubbish collected in your street?

We all throw away mountains of rubbish each week.

Many people think that throwing away rubbish is damaging the world we live in. If rubbish is sorted it can be recycled.

WHAT RUBBISH?

What kinds of rubbish do you throw away?

People who recycle rubbish are interested in what the rubbish is made of.

1 Write down the different materials your rubbish is made of.

2 For each material make a list of the actual items you throw away at home.

HOW MUCH GLASS?

How much glass do you throw away in a week?

Most glass is either bottles or jars.

1 Put the glass bottles or jars your family throws away in a large bag or box. Do this for seven days.

You can then find out how much glass you have collected.

You can measure this in several ways.

- You can count the number of bottles and jars.
- You can count the number of large bottles separately from the number of small bottles.
- You can find the total amount of liquid the bottles and jars hold.
- You can weigh the bottles.

2 Write down one thing for and one thing against each idea.

3 Decide which idea to use. Or you can use your own idea.

(a) How much glass does your family throw away in a week?

(b) How much of it is clear glass?

(c) How much of it is green glass?

(d) How much of it is brown glass?

WHAT COLOUR GLASS?

Each member of a class in Cornwall weighed the amount of glass their family threw away in one week. They weighed the clear glass, the green glass and the brown glass separately.

They put their results into a spreadsheet.

Here are the results. The weights are in kilograms.

Name	Clear	Green	Brown
Sir	0.61	0.73	0.00
Jason	1.10	0.40	0.00
Philip	0.70	0.00	1.30
Gareth	1.38	0.25	0.00
Keith	4.30	0.00	0.00
Simon	0.55	0.00	0.00
Damien	1.35	1.95	0.00
Heather	1.20	0.00	0.00
Emily	2.20	0.42	0.00
Andrew	7.70	0.00	3.30
Tristan	0.00	0.50	0.00
Emma	1.00	0.00	0.00
Sanjay	0.45	0.00	1.45
Julie	1.56	3.26	0.00
David	0.00	0.75	0.00
Sarah	1.00	0.00	0.00
Helen	1.22	0.00	0.00
Karl	2.00	1.00	0.00
Yasmin	2.00	0.00	0.00
Stephen	8.38	0.00	1.80

1 (*a*) Which family threw away most clear glass?

(*b*) Which family threw away most green glass?

(*c*) Which family threw away most brown glass?

  The total weight of glass collected by Jason's family was

1.10 + 0.40 + 0.00 = 1.5 kg.

2 (*a*) What was the total wight of glass collected by:

   (i)   Philip's family?

   (ii) Emma's family?

   (iii) Julie's family?

(*b*) Which family threw away the biggest amount of glass?

(*c*) Which family threw away the smallest amount of glass?

(*d*) Which families threw away only one sort of glass?

3 (*a*) What was the total amount of clear glass thrown away?

(*b*) What was the total amount of green glass thrown away?

(*c*) What was the total amount of brown glass thrown away?

(*d*) What was the total amount of glass thrown away?

 These are the results for Emily's family.

Clear glass 2.2 kg.
Total glass 2.62 kg.

To find the **percentage** of clear glass you need a calculator.

First *divide* 2.2 by 2.62.
Then *multiply* by 100.

| 2 | • | 2 | ÷ | 2 | • | 6 | 2 | × | 1 | 0 | 0 | = |

You should get 84% (it is sensible to give your answer as a whole number).

---

4 What percentage of the glass thrown away by

(*a*) Heather's family was clear?

(*b*) Sanjay's family was brown?

(*c*) Karl's family was green?

(*d*) Simon's family was clear?

5 (*a*) What percentage of the total glass thrown away by the whole class was clear?

(*b*) What percentage of the total glass thrown away was green?

(*c*) What percentage of the total glass thrown away was brown?

(*d*) Draw a pie chart to show the amounts of glass of different colours thrown away by the whole family.

You need the
resource sheet
*'Percentage pie
charts'* for
question 5(*d*).

WHAT COLOUR GLASS IN YOUR CLASS?

How much glass of each colour was thrown away by your class's families?

- Collect together the results for everyone in your class.
- Use the questions in the activity *'What colour glass?'* to analyse your class's results.
- Make a display of your findings. Use pictures or charts if these help to explain.
- How much glass do you estimate that the families of your class throw away in a year?

You could enter the results into a database or spreadsheet.

INDIVIDUAL DIFFERENCES

I Some families throw away a lot more glass than others.

Different families throw away glass of different colours.

One way of measuring how much difference there is between families is to use the **range.**

The **range** means the difference between the *most* and the *least*.

Look at the Cornwall results. Look at the clear glass thrown away by the *girls'* families.

Most   =   8.38 kg
Least   =   1 kg
Range   =   7.38 kg

1 (a) What was the most clear glass thrown away by one of the boys' families?

   (b) What was the least clear glass thrown away by one of the boys' families?

   (c) What was the range for clear glass thrown away by boys' families?

2 What is the range for green glass thrown away by all families?

3 What is the range for brown glass thrown away by all families?

Median amount
of clear glass.

> **I** What was the 'average' amount of clear glass thrown away by the Cornwall families? One way of measuring the 'average' is to use the **median.**
>
> To find the median, you first need to list the results in order of size.
>
> 0.00, 0.00, 0.45, 0.55, 0.61, 0.70, 1.00, 1.00, 1.10, 1.20, 1.22, 1.35, 1.38, 1.56, 2.00, 2.00, 2.20, 4.30, 7.70, 8.38
>
> The **median** amount means the *middle* amount.
>
> There are 20 numbers. So, there are two middle numbers: 1.20 and 1.22. The median is the 'average' of these middle numbers $(1.20 + 1.22) \div 2 = 1.21$.
>
> So, the median amount of clear glass is 1.21 kg.

4 What is the median amount of green glass thrown away by the Cornwall families?

5 What is the median amount of brown glass thrown away by the Cornwall families?

6 (*a*) What is the median amount of all glass thrown away by the girls' families?

   (*b*) What is the median amount of all glass thrown away by the boys' families?

   (*c*) Did the girls' families throw away more glass than the boys' families on average?

Mean amount
of clear glass.

> **I** A different way of finding the 'average' amount is to use the **mean.**
>
> To find the **mean** amount of clear glass thrown away by the Cornwall families:
>
> Total amount = 38.70 kg
> Number of families = 20
> Mean amount = $38.70 \div 20 = 1.93$ kg

7 What is the mean amount of green glass thrown away by the Cornwall families?

8 What is the mean amount of brown glass thrown away by the Cornwall families?

9 (*a*) What is the mean amount of all glass thrown away by the girls' families?

   (*b*) What is the mean amount of all glass thrown away by the boys' families?

   (*c*) Did the girls' families throw away more glass than the boys' families on average?

INDIVIDUAL DIFFERENCES IN YOUR CLASS

Use the questions in the activity *'Individual differences'* to analyse your class's results.

Add the results to your display.

- Did your family throw away more or less glass than the average amount for your class?

- Do you think your class is typical? Do other families throw away more glass or less glass than the families in your class? How could you find out?

BOTTLE BANKS

Many towns now have bottle banks into which you can throw glass rubbish. The glass is taken out of these banks and recycled.

The shapes and sizes of two bottle banks are shown in these pictures.

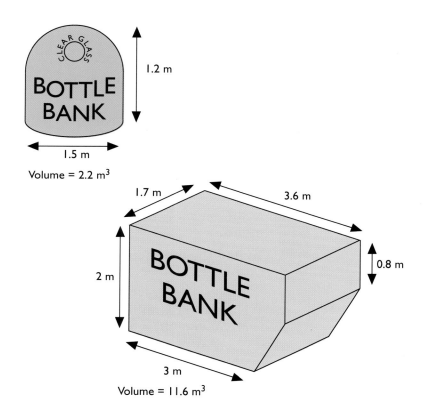

Volume = 2.2 m³

Volume = 11.6 m³

How much glass does one bottle bank hold?

129 page 163

One way to find out is to see how much glass you can get into a large cardboard box. You can then work out how many cardboard boxes would fit into the bottle bank.

RECYCLING GLASS IN YOUR TOWN

What is the population of the town you live in (or the nearest town)?

If everybody in your town wanted to recycle *all* their glass, estimate how much glass that would be in a week.

Estimate how many bottle banks your town would need, if each bank was emptied once a week.

SHOULD MORE RUBBISH BE RECYCLED?

Do you think more rubbish should be recycled?

How might more people be encouraged to use bottle banks?

Often bottle banks are in large car parks on the edge of towns. Is this a good place for them?

What other types of rubbish are recycled in your town?

REVIEW EXERCISES I

EXERCISE 26 Circles

1 The diameter of this big wheel is 10 m.

(a) How far do people go when the wheel turns once?

(b) During a ride the wheel turns round 15 times. How far do people go altogether?

2 A plate has a diameter of 24 cm. It is decorated with spots round the edge. The spots are about 2 cm apart.

How many spots are there?

3 This picture shows a metal frame for a window.

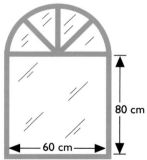

What is the length of the metal in the frame?

4 A car has wheels 57 cm in diameter. A woman drives the car 8 kilometres when she goes to work.

How many times do the wheel turn?

EXERCISE 27 Using letters

1 A robot obeys 4 instructions: N (north), S (south), E (east) and W (west).

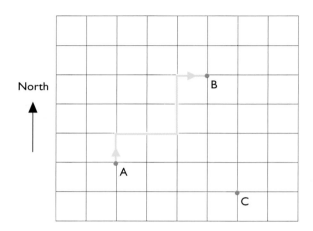

The picture shows one way the robot can get from A to B.

Here are the instructions

NEENE

(a) List the instructions to get the robot back from B to A, using the same route.

(b) List all the instructions to get the robot back from B to A using a different route.

(c) Do all the routes from B to A need the same number of instructions? Explain your answer.

(d) The robot starts at A, goes to C and then goes to B. What is the smallest number of instructions needed for this?

(e) Somebody else gives you the instructions for a route from A to C.

Invent a method of checking whether the instructions are correct without using the picture.

2 Here is a part of a honeycomb.

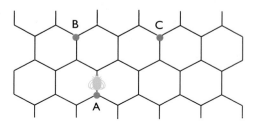

A bee starts at A in the direction of the arrow. Each time it comes to a junction it turns either left (L) or right (R).

Here is a route for it to get to B.

LR

(a) Write down a route from A to C.

(b) Write down several routes from A to B. All the routes should be a different length.

Can you find a route with 8 instructions?

Can you find a route with 7 instructions?

(c) Write down the *shortest* route starting at A and getting back to A. Is there more than one answer?

(d) Write down the *shortest* route starting at A, getting back to A and visiting C on the way. Is there more than one answer?

(e) Write down a shortest route from A to B to A.

(f) Write down a shortest route from A to B to A to B to A.

Is it twice as long as the shortest route for part (e)?

Explain your answer.

EXERCISE 28 Ordering numbers

1 Arrange the numbers in order, starting with the smallest.

   1, –2, 3, –4, 5, –6, 7, –8

2 Arrange these numbers in order, staring with the smallest.

   0.4, 0.8, 0.12, 1.2, 0.16, 1.6, 2.4, 2.12

3 Copy each of the lines shown and put the numbers given in the correct place.

   (a) 4, 6   (b) 40, 80, 130

   (c) 15, 21   (d) 0, 6

   (e) 1.5, 2.5, 4.25   (f) 10.6, 10.5, 10.95

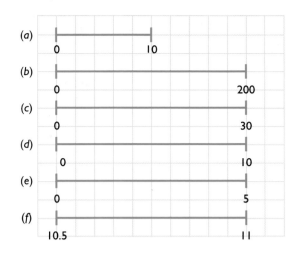

EXERCISE 29 Handling data 3

1 In 1989 £5161 million was spent on passenger transport. 95% of this was spent on road transport.

   How much was spent on road transport?

2 This tables shows how much different types of transport were used for carrying goods in Britain.

	1980 (1000 million tonne-km)	1989 (1000 million tonne-km)
Road	92.4	137.4
Rail	17.6	17.3
Pipe	10.1	9.4
Water	54.5	57.7

(a) How much goods travelled by road in 1989? Explain what the units mean.

(b) What was the total amount of goods movement in 1980 and in 1989?

(c) What percentage of goods movement in 1980 was by road? What percentage by rail? By pipe? By water?

(d) What percentage of goods movement in 1989 was by road? What percentage by rail? By pipe? By water?

(e) Which types of transport increased what they carried between 1980 and 1989?

(f) Which types of transport increased their percentage of the total goods carried between 1980 and 1989?

REVISION EXERCISES

REVISION EXERCISE I (Tasks 1–6)

1 (a) How many square numbers are there between 50 and 99?

(b) How many multiples of 8 are there between 50 and 99?

2 Here is a plan of a room.

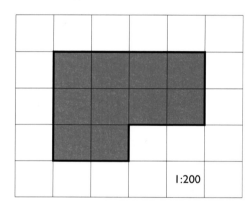

1:200

The scale of the plan is 1:200.
(a) Find the perimeter of the room.

(b) Find the area of the room.

3

	Hours of sunshine yesterday
Blackpool	☀ ☀ ☀ ☀
Bournemouth	☀ ☀ ☀ ◔
Cromer	☀ ☀ ☀ ☀ ◖

 = 2 hours sunshine

(a) Which resort had the most sunshine?

(b) How many hours sunshine did it have?

(c) Which resort had the least sunshine?

(d) How many hours sunshine did it have?

4

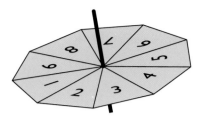

Someone spins this spinner.

(a) What is the probability that he gets an odd number?

(b) What is the probability that he gets a multiple of 3?

5

> ## WANTED
> Young person to work in shop on saturdays.
> 1 p.m. to 6 p.m. £2.25 per hour

Sam gets the job. How much does she earn each Saturday?

6 Its is Mira's twelfth birthday. How many days old is she?

REVISION EXERCISE II (Tasks 7–12)

1 (a) Draw axes on squared paper and plot these points:

A (4, 4), B (7, 2), C (2, 2), D (10, 2),
E (7, 5), F (6, –1), G (10, 5), H (7, 4)

(b) Name four points which are the corners of a square

(c) Name four points which are the corners of a parallelogram.

(d) Name four points which are the corners of a trapezium.

(e) Name three points which are the corners of a right-angled triangle.
(f) Name three points which are the corners of an isosceles triangle which is NOT right-angled.

(g) Which of the shapes you named in (b), (c), (d), (e) and (f) has the biggest area?

2 This picture shows a pie chart. It has not been drawn accurately.

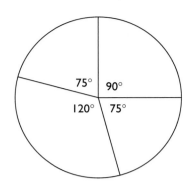

(a) Draw the pie chart accurately.

The pie chart represents the birth seasons of students in a class.

Most students were born in Spring.
The same number of students were born in Summer and in Winter.
The number of students born in Autumn is 6.

(b) Label the slices of the pie chart with the correct labels (Spring, Summer, Autumn and Winter).

(c) How many students are in the class?

(d) How many students were born in the Spring?

(e) How many students were born in the Winter?

(f) What percentage of students were born in the Autumn?

(g) What percentage of students were born in the Summer?

3 A toy train has an engine with 6 wheels and several coaches with 4 wheels.

(a) How many wheels does the train have if there are 2 coaches?

(b) How many wheels if there are 4 coaches?

(c) How many wheels if there are N coaches?

REVISION EXERCISE III (Tasks 13–18)

1 The equilateral triangle shown has sides of length 4 cm.

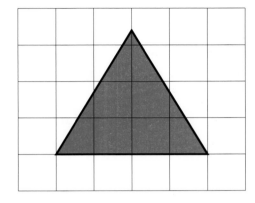

(a) What is the perimeter of the triangle?

(b) Estimate the area of the triangle.

2 Fill in the missing numbers.

(a) $43 + \square = 47$

(b) $430 + \square = 470$

(c) $3 \times \square = 18$

(d) $3 \times \square = 180$

(e) $10 \times \square = 100$

(f) $10 \times \square = 200$

(g) $10 \times \square = 3000$

(h) $12 \div \square = 60$

(i) $120 \div \square = 60$

(j) $120 \div \square = 6$

3 After a holiday 20 people were asked how many ice creams they had eaten. These are their replies.

3, 5, 1, 0, 0, 1, 10, 5, 2, 1, 2, 2, 4, 3, 2, 5, 6, 3, 4, 4

(a) What is the mode for this data?

(b) What is the median number of ice creams eaten?

(c) What is the mean number of ice creams eaten?

4 The picture shows two boards. In each board alternate squares are coloured red, starting at the bottom left.

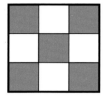
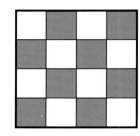

(a) Copy and complete this table.

Size of board	No. of squares coloured
1	
2	
3	5
4	
5	
6	

(b) Draw a flow chart to input the size of the board and output the number of squares coloured.

REVISION EXERCISE IV (Tasks 19–28)

1 Choose the correct answer.

(a) John walks to school. He walks
100 cm
100 m
100 km

(b) Kelly cycles to school. She cycles
$\frac{1}{2}$ an inch
$\frac{1}{2}$ a yard
$\frac{1}{2}$ a mile.

(c) Darren catches the bus. The bus travels
5000 inches
5000 m
5000 km
5000 miles.

2 Calculate

(a) $2^1 - 1^2$ (b) $3^2 - 2^3$

(c) $4^3 - 3^4$ (d) $5^4 - 4^5$

3 Pick out the biggest from each pair.

(a) $\frac{1}{4}$ and 40%

(b) $\frac{2}{5}$ and 25%

(c) $\frac{3}{4}$ and 0.34

(d) $\frac{1}{8}$ and 8%

(e) $\frac{8}{9}$ and 0.8

4 Here is a recipe for danish apple pudding for 4 people:

4 oz butter	2 oz raisins or sultanas
4 oz sugar	2 dessertspoons brown sugar
8 oz flour	1 oz peanuts
1 egg	12 oz cooking apples
	$\frac{1}{4}$ teaspoon salt

(a) Change the recipe so that it is for 8 people.

(b) Change the recipe so that it is for 2 people.

5 Each of these shapes are made out of a piece of wire:

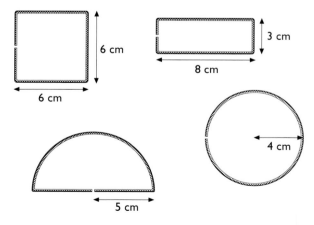

(a) Which shape uses most wire?

(b) Which shape uses least wire?

6 What 16-year-old school leavers did in 1991.

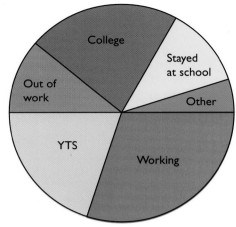

(a) What did fewest leavers do?

(b) What was the commonest thing leavers did?

(c) Use a protractor to help you find what percentage of leavers were out of work.

REVISION EXERCISE V (Tasks 1–28)

1 (a) Jim gets paid £140 for a 40 hour week. How much does he earn each hour?

(b) Mary gets paid £180 for a 50 hour week. How much does she earn each hour?

2 (a) How many minutes is each of your lessons?

(b) How many minutes' work do you do at school in a week?

3 How many pets do you have?

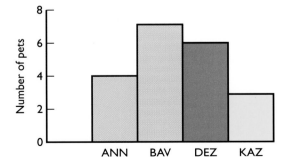

(a) Which of the children has the most pets?

(b) How many pets do the children have altogether?

4

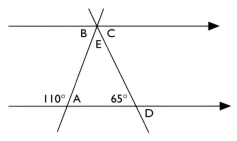

What is the size of the angles A, B, C, D and E?

5 Arrange these in order of how likely they are.

Start with the most likely.

A It will snow tomorrow
B The date tomorrow is 30th February
C Someone will say 'Hello' to me tomorrow.
D Someone in Britain has a birthday tomorrow
E I shall fall over on the way home from school today.
F Next time I spin a coin I shall get a head.
G Next time I throw a dice I shall get a 6.
H Next time I go to the shop I shall get the wrong change.

6 John walks to the record shop. This is his route.

He turns right out of his front gate.
He turns left by the post box.
He goes straight on at the cross roads.
At the traffic lights he turns left and then right.
He turns right at the station.
The record shop is on the right-hand side of the road.

Describe John's route home from the record shop.

7 Sanjay spins a 20p coin, a 50p coin and a £1 coin. He sees which are heads and which are tails.

Here is one possibility.

(a) List all the possibilities.

(b) What is the probability that all the coins will be heads?

8

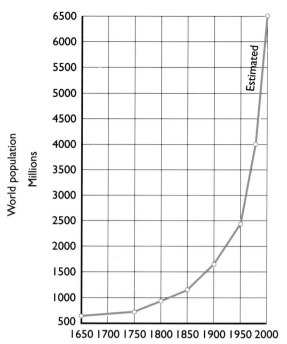

(a) What was the world population in 1980?

(b) What is the estimated world population in 2000?

(c) What was the world population in 1650?

9 This design is made from wire.

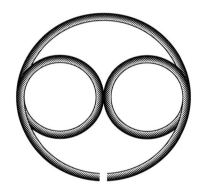

The diameter of the biggest circle is 1 m.

The design is then taken apart and all the wire is used to make one circle.

What is the diameter of this circle?

10 Here are two regular polygons.

In each polygon diagonals have been drawn from one corner.

(a) Copy and complete this table:

Number of sides of polygon	Number of diagonals from one corner
3	
4	
5	2
6	
7	

(b) How many diagonals are there from one corner of a regular polygon with N sides?

(c) In each of these polygons all the diagonals have been drawn.

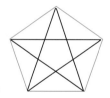 

Copy and complete this table:

Number of sides of polygon	Number of diagonals
3	
4	
5	5
6	
7	

(d) How many diagonals are there altogether in a regular polygon with N sides?